Hello!

DEVON

Edited by Allison Dowse

First published in Great Britain in 2000 by
YOUNG WRITERS
Remus House,
Coltsfoot Drive,
Woodston,
Peterborough, PE2 9JX
Telephone (01733) 890066

HB ISBN 0 75431 980 6
SB ISBN 0 75431 981 4

FOREWORD

This year, the Young Writers' Up, Up & Away competition proudly presents a showcase of the best poetic talent from over 70,000 up-and-coming writers nationwide.

Successful in continuing our aim of promoting writing and creativity in children, our regional anthologies give a vivid insight into the thoughts, emotions and experiences of today's younger generation, displaying their inventive writing in its originality.

The thought, effort, imagination and hard work put into each poem impressed us all and again the task of editing proved challenging due to the quality of entries received, but was nevertheless enjoyable. We hope you are as pleased as we are with the final selection and that you continue to enjoy *Up, Up & Away Devon* for many years to come.

CONTENTS

Charlotte Bower	55
Laura Duncan	56
Adam Yersin	56
Donna Walsh	57
Brittany Caunter	58
Kieran James	58
Hannah Caunter	59
Mikaela Boarer	60
Annabel Mitchell	60
Max Pontin	61
Zack Bevan	61
Cara Hendriksen	62
Rebekah Glanvill	63

Exeter Cathedral School

Matthew Hale	63
Catriona Rodger	64
Jessica Wood	64
Rebecca Westley	65
Ashleigh-Jade Black	65
Lara-Clare Bourdeaux	66
Daniel Jones	66
Freddy Barnes	67
Naomi Sourbut	67
Sean Flynn	68
Archie Miller	68
Thomas Rainey	68
Camilla Biggs	69
Tobi Herpoldt McCrone	69
Aurora Moxon	70

Greylands Prep School

Katy Cooper	70
Michael Tucker	71
Joshua Mason	71
Sally Pickering	72
James Parish	72
William Perrett	72

Kathryn Morris	73
Cara Duerden	73
Rebecca Hadley	74
George Harris	74
Daniel Vaughton	75

Hennock Community Primary School

Kallie Johnson	75
Joanna Newton	76
Christine Seward	76
Rachel Martin	77
Henry Harvey	77

Manor House School

Alexander Hayden	77
Paul Holborow	78
Sophie Collett	78
James Horman	79
Ben Matthews	79
Amy Channing	80
Rupert Perry	80
Phillippa Frost	81
Harriet Carr	81
BJ Man	82
Daniel Rowe	82
Laura Young	83
Ben Brown	83
Sam Lockwood	84
Hannah Sweet	84
Michael Yaskin	85
Ciaran Feeney	85
Katya Moore	86
Alex Hasell	86
Heather Moore	87
Charles Coundley	87
Nicholas Manning	88
Katharine Manning	89
Ginny Baker	90

Tedburn St Mary Primary School

The Maynard School

Kim Saddler	184
Esther Tillson	184
Lucy Bayliss	185
Katy Woolley	186
Jennifer Doe	187
Charlotte McDermid	188
Roxanne Saunders	189
Claudia Shaw	190
Sarah Quicke	191
Pippa Black	191
Naomi Pankhurst	192

Tipton St John Primary School

Rosa Bonifacii	193
Laura Clapp	193
Asher Smyth	194
Emma Carruthers	194
Susannah Moore	195
Megan Thomas	196
Claire Rule	197

Two Moors Primary School

Neal Clapp	197
Meg Menheneott	198
Rhiannon Babb	198
Daniel Cottrell	199
Cally Harris	200
Sam Isaacs	200
Nikita Harrison	201
Deborah Toon	201
Natalie Burnage	202
Robert Willis	202
Chris Baker	203
Daisy Clark	203
Nico Cruwys	204
Emily Warren	204
Linsey Williams	204

Yeo Valley Primary School

Bethany Hall	220
Kim Rogers	221
Bethany Angell	221
Katie L Pink	222
Latisha Collins	222
Josh Yeo	222
Claire Harris	223
Terri Sheppard	223
Laura Matthewson	224
Jennifer White	224
Kylie Bamsby	224
Drew Owens	225
Matthew Hitchins	225
Samantha Lewis	226
Mark Palmer	226
Laura Ellis	227
Nathan Windsor	227
Emma Mason	228
Esther Elizabeth Prosser	228
Sam Harley	228
Rachel Wait	229
Sophie Hawkins	229

The Poems

FLOWERS

In spring
The snow-white snowdrop and sky-blue bluebell,
Announce themselves by waving merrily to the birds.
Hark!
The daffodil blows its golden trumpet,
Next comes the yellow middled daisy,
Playing with the pale primrose
And the pure yellow dandelion.

In summer
The beautiful lily gracefully sails across the deep blue lake,
Roses all colours, in sprays in gardens,
Or wild in leafy, green hedges.
Forget-me-nots and love-in-a-mist so blue,
Our daisy welcomes them all.

In autumn
The flowers are going to sleep
While watching the golden orange leaves tumble.
All our colourful, pretty, seasonal friends are sleeping,
That is except the tough little daisy.

In winter
Most flowers are gone,
Except for one which goes on and on,
With its pure yellow middle
And cold white petals,
The small tough daisy goes on all year!

Charlotte Hobbs (9)

THE FUNFAIR

Fun is the life of a boy!
Gun shoots!
'Win a teddy!'
It makes you happy!
And the big wheel
Goes round and round,
and there's 'Freddy's Revenge' -
Not that scary!
And the ghost house -
Well, everybody knows
There's no such thing.
And then home time.
But before we go
we're allowed an ice-cream.
Then the fun's gone.

Edward Jones (10)
Bendarroch School

LITTLE MAN

Up, up and away
Where the sky is grey,
A little man lives
Only a mile away.

I said to the little man,
'Where do you fly?'
Said I.
But he did not answer
So I did not try!

Carys Davies (8)
Bendarroch School

MY GRANDPA

I was six when my grandpa died
And I cried and cried and cried,

Lots of things I wanted to say
But there was not to be another day.

I could not see him again,
Oh, I can feel the pain,

He used to use a walking stick
But when he was young he was quite quick.

He played in Three Crosses Rugby Team
For that was his dream.

So now I see
That he is so special to me.

Siân Davies (10)
Bendarroch School

AUTUMN LEAVES

Twisting, turning, swirling in multicoloured showers,
These are autumn's flowers.
Red, orange, gold and brown,
These are the colours that fall on the ground.

Lying on the streets,
Ready to greet,
That one great leap,
That sends you flying into the heap, crunch, snap, crack.

The rain comes down and you run back,
Into your house to watch,
The colours fading, like a battery running out in a torch.

Zoë Watts (11)
Bendarroch School

MONDAY MORNING

The baby's crying,
The cat's pooing,
The rain is pouring,
Grandad's snoring,
The dog is barking,
The eggs are frying,
The guinea pig's feeding,
The rabbit's sneezing,
The TV's blasting,
The radio's partying,
The kettle's boiling,
The toaster's popping,
The crumpet's roasting.
The neighbours are shouting . . .
It's just hell round here!

Caitlin Cornwell (10)
Bendarroch School

THE HEDGEHOG

The hedgehog scuttled into the leaves
As the sun streamed in
At the gaps in the trees.
An insect crawled past him
And disappeared.
He pricked his ears
And plodded into a bush.

Polly Luce (9)
Bendarroch School

THE DOG THAT I DIDN'T GET

When I was a tiny little boy
To swim I tried my best,
I practised oh so many weeks
To reach my very first test.

My parents they had promised me,
A dog, should I succeed
To swim two or three lengths maybe
For me to hold that lead.

Now I can swim on my front
And on my back - all styles, in fact
For as long as you like, for as far as you like -
Swimming is now completely hacked.

My brother David can now swim like me.
Where's my dog that was promised originally?
Said my mum, 'At the end of the year we're moving to France,
Perhaps a dog then, there's maybe a chance.'

Once we are there
We've been promised many things new.
I'll let you know by postcard
If any come true.

Matthew Kernick (9)
Bendarroch School

SKY SWEEPER

The enchanted black horse that sweeps the sky,
Singing a song - a melody that will never die,
Covered with sequins, pink and peach,
To all houses her clutches reach,
To drop dust upon the sleepy eyes,
Of those who dream about the skies.
As dusk appears she takes to flight,
Soaring in the starry night.
Her tail is long, her mane is black,
She lives upon the moon, in a shack.
The magic glaze about her eyes,
Ripples round her as she flies,
The velvet stars, the silky moon,
She conjures up dreams, to send soon,
To knock the heads of those who creep,
Up to the window when they can't sleep,
To look up at the wondrous skies,
And as they stare,
Moonbeams gather in their eyes.
For those who sleep they will miss out,
For they won't see the satin horses superb mount,
So she bids you well, who stay to watch her,
Bounding onward, but in her clutches she now nurtures,
A foal, just like herself in size,
With exactly the same magic glaze in her eyes.

Deya Brown (11)
Bendarroch School

LION

Inside the shaggy mat of turf, the wind howling wildly.
Inside the wind howling wildly, the prickly thorns.
Inside the prickly thorns, the brightness of evil.
Inside the brightness of evil, the wet patch of dew.
Inside the wet patch of dew, the mountains of saliva.
Inside the mountains of saliva, the touch of flesh.
Inside the touch of flesh, the whimper of departure.
Inside the whimper of departure, the vicious howl of pride.
Inside the vicious howl of pride, the offspring yelps.
Inside the offspring yelps, the help of a distant shadow.
Inside the help of a distant shadow, the triumph of treachery.
Inside the triumph of treachery, the intimidated panic.
Inside the intimidated panic, the pricked points of death.
Inside the pricked points of death, the shaggy mat of turf.

Hayley Jolly (10)
Bere Alston Primary School

CAT

Inside the cat's eye, the bowl of fish,
Inside the bowl of fish, the cat's mouth,
Inside the cat's mouth, the taste of milk,
Inside the taste of milk, a fur-ball of fur.
Inside a fur-ball of fur, a purr of a baby kitten,
Inside a purr of a baby kitten, the love of a mum,
Inside the love of a mum, the warmth of her fur,
Inside the warmth of her fur, the tiptoe of her foot,
Inside the tiptoe of her foot, the night's silence,
Inside the night's silence, the cat's eye.

Kally Laing (10)
Bere Alston Primary School

MY DOG MEARNSY

Mearnsy,
>His automatic cheesy smile that's used when
>his skinny belly is tickled or hit,
>his bark as loud as roaring machinery that's
>ploughing a field of corn.

Mearnsy,
>His white fur, getting muddy as fast as someone
>getting sucked into in-breathing sinking mud,
>and as soft as a newborn baby's skin.

Mearnsy,
>His beady eyes used as a light bulb in the night,
>and puffed when walkies or yum-yums are
>the mentioned words.

Mearnsy,
>His morning hello is a jump, kiss and a paws-up
>to greet me.

Judith Mortimer (11)
Bere Alston Primary School

HEDGEHOG

Inside the gardeners' heaven, the ball of needles.
Inside the ball of needles, the hedgehog's twitching nose.
Inside the hedgehog's twitching nose, the snuffling of leaves.
Inside the snuffling of leaves, the ocean of grass.
Inside the ocean of grass, the hedgehog's larder.
Inside the hedgehog's larder, the feast of summer.
Inside the feast of summer, the gardeners' heaven.

Rebecca Ward (11)
Bere Alston Primary School

INSIDE

Inside the tree trunk the parrot's nest
Inside the parrot's nest the bright feathers
Inside the bright feathers the blue sky
Inside the blue sky the white clouds
Inside the white clouds the yellow sun
Inside the yellow sun the parrot's feathers
Inside the parrot's feathers the berry juice
Inside the berry juice the parrot's beak
Inside the parrot's beak the brown nut
Inside the brown nut the tree trunk
Inside the tree trunk the parrot's nest.

Megan Dunsby (11)
Bere Alston Primary School

RABBITS

Inside the rabbit's eye, a black hole.
Inside the black hole, the rabbit's fur.
Inside the rabbit's fur, a smooth river.
Inside the smooth river, the rabbit's saliva.
Inside the rabbit's saliva, a drop of blood.
Inside the drop of blood, the rabbit's tongue.
Inside the rabbit's tongue, a bumpy lane.
Inside the bumpy lane, the rabbit's teeth.
Inside the rabbit's teeth, a drop of frost,
Inside the drop of frost, the rabbit's eye.

Tanneth Smith (11)
Bere Alston Primary School

INSIDE THE WOLF

Inside the wolf's ear, the sound of prey.
Inside the sound of prey, the wolf's drool.
Inside the wolf's drool, the crunch of bones.
Inside the crunch of bones, the wolf's howl.
Inside the wolf's howl, a silhouette against the moon.
Inside a silhouette against the moon, the wolf's face.
Inside the wolf's face, a sly grin.
Inside the sly grin, the wolf's eye.
Inside the wolf's eye, the drooping slumber.
Inside the drooping slumber, the wolf's breath.
Inside the wolf's breath, his sudden wakefulness.
Inside his sudden wakefulness, the sound of footsteps.
Inside the sound of footsteps, the clang of a trap.
Inside the clang of a trap, the wolf's ear.

Stacey Clayton (10)
Bere Alston Primary School

MUM

Her face is like a beautiful flower blooming in the garden,
Her eyes are as bright as a light in a dark room,
Her smile is as warming as a fire on a cold day,
She dresses like an angel floating up to Heaven,
Her hug is a warming blanket wrapping around me,
When she is happy she glows like a star,
She starts cooking and nothing can stop her,
When she talks smoothly I nearly fall asleep,
When she plays with me she is so much fun.

Karen Daymond (11)
Bere Alston Primary School

EAGLE

Inside the eagle's eye, the hastening food.
Inside the hastening food, the pounding heart.
Inside the pounding heart, the flapping of wings.
Inside the flapping of wings, the layer of feathers.
Inside the layer of feathers, the soft cry of a child.
Inside the soft cry of a child, the seagull's flutter.
Inside the seagull's flutter, the fish of the deep.
Inside the fish of the deep, the inky dark void.
Inside the inky dark void, the inanimate captor.
Inside the inanimate captor, the murderous shriek.
Inside the murderous shriek, the tiger's haunting growl.
Inside the tiger's haunting growl, the eagle's prey.
Inside the eagle's prey, the Circle of Life.
Inside the Circle of Life, the eagle's eye.

Cede Gadsby (10)
Bere Alston Primary School

GRANDAD

His hair as curly as twisted pasta, greasy like olive oil,
His face all browny-red like a suntan,
It's wrinkled like an old tomato crinkled on the worktop which
Has been left there for days, he's full of smiles!

His glorious eyes have a latticed affect beside each eye,
Sparkling in the glistening sunlight,
His old cranked crispy voice is like a mouth full of crackling corn,
His heart is full of kindness, sharing thoughts.
He enjoys his dark frothy black Guinness every day.

And that is why I love my grandad.

Tiffy Adair (10)
Bere Alston Primary School

DARK AND LIGHT

Such a dark sky
But one bright star
Sits lonely above a little soft cloud
A tiny little diamond
In the sky
An only child
Of the great full moon
Sun in the morning
Such blinding light
Out of bed
Blinded by the brightness
Outdoors to school
And back into darkness
Hours after.

Kerry Wright (11)
Bere Alston Primary School

INSIDE

Inside the winter's frost the cold hands of a lonely child.
Inside the cold hands of a lonely child the warmth of a coal fire.
Inside the warmth of a coal fire the sound of a celebrating family.
Inside the sound of a celebrating family the whoosh of a thrown
snowball.
Inside the whoosh of a thrown snowball the suffering of a starving bird.
Inside the suffering of a starving bird the ice of a deserted frozen lake.
Inside the ice of a deserted frozen lake the winter's frost.

Jonathan Walker (11)
Bere Alston Primary School

CAT

Inside the cat's mouth, a tunnel of air.
Inside the tunnel of air, the cat's fur.
Inside the cat's fur, a load of fleas.
Inside the cat's fleas, the sharp teeth.
Inside the sharp teeth, a mountain of crystal.
Inside the mountain of crystal, a stream of fishes.
Inside the stream of fishes, the cat's mouth.

Luke Viggers (10)
Bere Alston Primary School

PUPPY

Inside the puppy's fur, the moving forest.
Inside the moving forest, the bouncy skin.
Inside the bouncy skin, the river of blood.
Inside the river of blood, the puppy's tail.
Inside the puppy's tail, the rotting rock.
Inside the rotting rock, the smooth gum.
Inside the smooth gum, the puppy.

James Jewell (10)
Bere Alston Primary School

BATS

Inside the bat's mouth the wing of a moth.
Inside the wing of a moth the vein of a river.
Inside the vein of a river a twig of a tree.
Inside a twig of a tree a sharp claw.
Inside a sharp claw a cut of a thorn.
Inside a cut of a thorn the bat's mouth.

Della Moloney (11)
Bere Alston Primary School

My Nan

My nan,
Sweet as a buttercup.
Her face just sits there smiling all day and night.
A few crinkles and dimples.
Her lips red as a rose.

My nan
Always doing the gardening.
A sweet smell of pansies and daisies.
Muddy hands, dirty as a coalman.

My nan
Often likes to buy toffees,
Sucking them like a vacuum cleaner.
The day is over and she'll have forty winks.

My nan is the number one nan.

Stephanie Falconer (11)
Bere Alston Primary School

The Cat

Inside the cat's fur a soft creature.
Inside the soft creature the warm blood.
Inside the warm blood a wink of an eye.
Inside the wink of an eye the cat's nose.
Inside the cat's nose a gentle touch.
Inside a gentle touch the cat's tongue.
Inside the cat's tongue the cat's body.
Inside the cat's body a soft creature.

Shakira Sandhu (10)
Bere Alston Primary School

CHIMPANZEE

I am
a hairy man,
a playful friend,
a swing king.

Fur coats for fashion,
Just let us live,
We don't mean to harm you.

I have
childish acts,
a cheeky grin,
naughty habits.

Fur coats for fashion,
Let us live,
We don't mean to harm you.

I am
an intelligent creature.
I have
a cute shape.

Don't harm us!

Victoria Russon (10)
Bere Alston Primary School

CRY OF THE WOLF

The wolf, hunter of deer, deliverer of fear.
    We despise him - for what?
The wolf, king of the forest, strong and proud.
    We despise him - for what?
The wolf, killer of weak, leaver of healthy.
    We despise him - for what?
The wolf, fast as a horse, fur so coarse.
    We despise him - for what?
The wolf, hearing as sharp as a knife.
    We despise him - for what?
The wolf, clever and cunning.
    We despise him - for what?
The wolf, member of a pack, working as a team.
    We despise him - for what?
The wolf, creature of a dream.
    We despise him - for what?
The wolf, lord of the night.

Finbar Rickman (10)
Bere Alston Primary School

THE FOX

The cunning fox.
The red-headed rascal.
The white tipped, bushy-tailed scavenger.
The nose to sniff out the enemy.
The claws to capture the victim.
The fangs of death to kill the prey.
The territory to be fought for, along with the vixen.
The hunter to be hunted.
The burning bright fur hanging in the shed of death.

Sarah Batten (10)
Bere Alston Primary School

INSIDE THE CAT'S EYE

Inside the cat's eye is a shining star.
Inside the shining star is the cat's claw.
Inside the cat's claw is the squeak of a mouse.
Inside the squeak of a mouse is a curious cat.
Inside the curious cat is the humming of a bee.
Inside the humming of a bee is a car's engine.
Inside the car's engine is the cat's purr.
Inside the cat's purr is the cat's love.
Inside the cat's love is the cat's tear.
Inside the cat's tear is a running stream.
Inside the running stream is a reflection.
Inside the reflection is the cat's eye.

Elliott Youel (10)
Bere Alston Primary School

CATS

Inside the cat's ear, the base drum.
Inside the base drum, the sandy tongue.
Inside the sandy tongue, the fish's tear.
Inside the fish's tear, the river of blood.
Inside the river of blood, the street of fleas.
Inside the street of fleas, the sharpest claw.
Inside the sharpest claw, the bony ground.
Inside the bony ground, the cat's ear.

William Ralph (11)
Bere Alston Primary School

INSIDE

Inside the staring eyes, the dark eclipse.
Inside the dark eclipse, the bitter weather.
Inside the bitter weather, the badger's sett.
Inside the badgers sett, the dusty tunnel.
Inside the dusty tunnel, the badger's nose.
Inside the badger's nose, the blood of the mouse.
Inside the blood of the mouse, the echoing squeak.
Inside the echoing squeak, the badger's teeth.
Inside the badger's teeth, the hard bone.
Inside the hard bone, the badger's paw.
Inside the badger's paw, the footprint in the mud.
Inside the footprint in the mud, the badger's eyes.

Jim McKenzie (11)
Bere Alston Primary School

TIGERS, TIGERS

Tigers, tigers, save them please, can't you see us on our knees?
Watch the stripes fall off in numbers, your stripes upon our
                                        woollen jumpers.
We try to save you day and night, although you always try to fight.
You may just think it's all for fun, with the hunter with his gun
but you will have to run and run.

Daryl Hughes (11)
Bere Alston Primary School

SLUG

In the slug's trail, cold, icy road.
In the cold, icy road, slug's skin.
In the slug's skin, school gruel.
In the school gruel, slug's eyes.
In the slug's eyes, a pinhead.
In a pinhead, a reflection.
In the reflection, a lake of water.
In a lake of water, slug's fear.
In the slug's fear, the human being.
In the human being, a leaf of cress.
In a leaf of cress, a slug's mouth.
In the slug's mouth, leaf's juice.
In the leaf's juice, the slug's trail.

Stephanie Portlock (11)
Bere Alston Primary School

UNTITLED

Inside the unicorn's horn, the forest of fairies.
Inside the forest of fairies, the unicorn's mouth.
Inside the unicorn's mouth, the stream of clear water.
Inside the stream of clear water, the unicorn's hoof.
Inside the unicorn's hoof, the leaves of trees.
Inside the leaves of trees, the unicorn's eye.
Inside the unicorn's eye, the star of birth.
Inside the star of birth, the unicorn's horn.

Gemma Doidge (11)
Bere Alston Primary School

INSIDE THE LION'S MANE

Inside the lion's mane, the cornfield.
Inside the cornfield, the lion's tail.
Inside the lion's tail, the swift sway.
Inside the swift sway, the lion's foot.
Inside the lion's foot, the deer's blood.
Inside the deer's blood, the lion's love.
Inside the lion's love, the pure heart.
Inside the pure heart, the lion's mane.

Matthew Stone (10)
Bere Alston Primary School

PUFF THE SMOKING DRAGON

I was walking down my lane one day
when I saw a dragon smoking,
I told him to pack it in but
instead Puff started choking,
He was choking on the tar which now
Puff always regrets,
And from now on Puff stays away
from cigarettes,
But the other day Puff did it again and I
saw him and this time I just ignored him,
I saw Puff in the hospital, he was really bad.
And Puff's little boy said, 'Don't worry'
and before he passed away Puff said,
'Never smoke lad, you'll end up dead.'

Chloe Sheppard (10)
Caen County Primary School

MY HAMSTER

My hamster gnaws,
My hamster stores.
Pit-a-pat, pit-a-pat,
My hamster's feet.
Eek, eek,
My hamster's squeak,
Chewing, nibbling, awake all night.

My hamster gnaws, *clang, clang.*
My hamster stores, *nibble, nibble.*
My hamster uses his wheel, *k-ting, k-ting.*
Awake all day is me,
Awake all night is he.

Charlotte May (9)
Caen County Primary School

THE FUN BEACH

The beach is my favourite place,
It's got so much wide open space,
You can run, shout and scream,
Eat lots of ice-cream.
There's always a smile on my face!

The sea is freezing, the sand is soft,
The dunes' reeds are spiky,
They cut my friend, Micky.

Natasha Holtmann (9)
Caen County Primary School

THE DEVIOUS LITTLE LIAR

This boy you never want to meet,
He tells lies so sweet,
The devious little liar,
He runs round his house shouting,
'Fire, fire.'
He's not funny,
He's not an angel from Heaven,
He's more like a bat out of Hell.
The devious little liar
Set all the teachers on fire,
(So would I to be honest).
That devious little liar
Who set all the teachers on fire.

Abbey Hopkins (9)
Caen County Primary School

MY HOT AIR BALLOON RIDE

Up and away into the sky,
Looking down at the fields from way up high.
The blustery wind brushes through my hair,
Making me shiver, but I don't care.
Silently the birds pass me by,
Warming my heart as they climb high.
But it's time to descend,
Time to go home,
But I'll remember
My special time alone.

Josie Kliem (9)
Caen County Primary School

DARK AND MISTY FIELD

What happened in a dark and misty field?
Was it a knight with sword and shield?

What is happening in a dark and misty field?
Is it trees blowing in the breeze?

What will be happening in a dark and misty field?
Meteorites, spacemen or UFOs? Nobody knows.

Suzanne Tomlinson (10)
Caen County Primary School

THE RAINBOW

Red, orange, green and blue,
Also indigo and violet too.

There's meant to be a pot of gold,
Well that's what I've been told.

Rainbows come when there's sun and rain,
It's called a rainbow and that's its name.

Courtney Holbourn (9)
Caen County Primary School

THE CAROL SINGERS

Every year, on Christmas Eve,
The carol singers, you will perceive,
Will come and sing their songs so sweet,
Their objective: to get something to eat.
But this year, this particular Noel,
They didn't sing them very well.

Ben Beresford West (9)
Caen County Primary School

TIGER

I saw a tiger at the zoo,
It looked like this:
Teeth like knives,
A tail like a bush,
It pounced as high as a sycamore tree.

A roar like thunder,
Its black stripes are black as coal.
Its orange stripes are bright as the sun.

Its claws as sharp as razors,
It looked as soft as sand,
And a nose as wet as the water.

Amber Winter (10)
Caen County Primary School

A SNAKE

A snake slithers and slides silently
through sand and leaves,
a snake curves, curls, bends and weaves,
swallows its prey like drinking water,
like a cruel, bloody and nasty slaughterer.
It has silky skin,
just like a dolphin's fin.
Its hiss sounds like lightning,
It's very frightening!
Sssssssssss!

Katie Gilpin (10)
Caen County Primary School

MY DOG SCRUFF

My dog scruff
Lives in my home.
I love him so much,
He is really nice to touch.
Hiding in his basket,
Looking for his bone.
Chewing on his slipper,
Taking it nice and slow.
We are very cheerful,
Sometimes even tearful.
I love him,
And he loves me,
We're a happy family.

Sophie Loxterkamp (9)
Caen County Primary School

OUR HOUSE

'Clean that mess up.'
'But he did it.'
'No I didn't!'
'What's for tea?'
'I want fish fingers.'
'Up those apple and pears
And clean your room up.'
'Can I watch TV?'
'No, you can't.'
'Can I have some money?'
'No!'

Callum Williams (10)
Caen County Primary School

RAINBOW PARROT

His feathers are like jumping into a rainbow.
His beak is as sharp as a fox's tail.
His feet are lethal.
He flies as smooth as an eagle.
He owns the lands.
Soaring through the skies,
Standing out like a rainbow.
Falling down like a lost soul
In the middle of the desert.

Simon Coles (10)
Caen County Primary School

THE FAIR

The fair is a lovely place to go
because of candyfloss, rides and the
fun you have too.

You've got swirly rides, scary rides, fun rides
and bouncy rides but the other one I like too
is the side to side ride that makes you go *'Whooooo.'*

Natalie Hall (10)
Caen County Primary School

A GIRAFFE

A giraffe is very tall, in fact it's so tall that it is as tall as a tree,
It's legs are as long as can be, can be, can be,
And its legs are as long as can be.
It has eyes that are so small they look like chocolate drops
And its tail swishes like the wind, the wind, the wind,
And its tail swishes like the wind.
Giraffe have feet so small they look like giant Smarties.
His ears are small like 2-d triangles.
Its face, well, its face is kind of oval, yeah its face is kind of an oval
shape.

Ceri Badge (10)
Caen County Primary School

LION

They have teeth like spikes,
Their eyes like black and yellow balls.

A mouth a big as a football.
A body as long as two tables.

A tail one metre long with
A little fluff on the end of it.

The teeth as sharp as two swords.

Tom Synnott (10)
Caen County Primary School

BRAINSTORMING

Think, think, think, I must start
Without damaging my heart.
Nuclear bomb going off in my brain,
Dynamite hiding all the pain.
Atlas, dictionary, book, book, book,
Please can I take a quick look?
Brain popping, brain bubbling, angry and storming,
I think that this is so boring.
Thunder, lightning and brain blasting,
Stupidly using my brain, never lasting.
Screaming and shouting,
Totally hating
Having to do all this
        Work, work, work!

Tara Walker (10)
Canada Hill Primary School

CHOCOLATE

I love Milky Way,
I'd love to get them every day.
Mum's got me a chocolate bar,
I'll keep it in my special jar.
When I'm hungry I'll eat it,
Not in my room though, it's a pit.
Rumble, rumble went my tum,
Yummy, yummy I've eaten it, *yum!*
Yum, yum went my tum.

Sammie Jo Cantor (10)
Canada Hill Primary School

MOTOR CROSS

The motorbikes are here,
They're burning over jumps,
Every time they're near,
They go over huge bumps,
Their front wheels goes up high,
But they never ever, ever die.

They burn it up in a jump,
They look up at the sky,
They land with a bump,
And flick mud up high,
Then they hit a large bump,
And fall off with a sigh.

Luke Hickie (11)
Canada Hill Primary School

UP, UP AND AWAY

Up, up and away,
Soaring through the sky.
Birds flying here and there,
The wind blowing through my hair.
Passing planes, helicopters,
Noisy things like that.
One day the wind blew
Away my hat.

Callum Nicholls (9)
Canada Hill Primary School

THE LITTLE COCOA BEAN

I'm a little cocoa bean
Hanging in a tree,
I'm a little cocoa bean,
You cannot eat me.

I'm a little cocoa bean,
Being all ground up,
I'm a little cocoa bean
In a little cup.

I'm a little cocoa bean,
Mixing with fresh milk,
I'm a little cocoa bean,
Soft and smooth as silk.

I'm a little chocolate bar
Waiting on a shelf,
I'm a little chocolate bar,
I can taste myself.

So eat me quick!

Elly Smith (10)
Canada Hill Primary School

POEMS

I'm not a poem person,
In fact I hate to rhyme,
Poetry's not my profession,
Instead I like aggression,
Fighting and crime, in mime!

Thomas Bougourd (10)
Canada Hill Primary School

WHY DINOSAUR WHY?

'Dinosaur, dinosaur,
Why do you eat?
Why do you eat people's feet?

Dinosaur, dinosaur,
You don't need to be mad.
Dinosaur, dinosaur,
You don't need to be bad.

Dinosaur, dinosaur,
What do you eat?'
'I eat you, because you're meat.'

Claire Taylor (10)
Canada Hill Primary School

DINO THE DINOSAUR

Dinosaurs big, dinosaurs bold,
Dinosaurs silky, wet and cold,
He may not hurt you he's a big balloon,
But watch out for Dino the goon.

He has *massive* feet, don't tell me I know,
He has to have a *massive* glow,
Every time you walk you make a *kablam,*
Your mum always said you look like a lamb.

But your not!

Sean Beeks (10)
Canada Hill Primary School

SWEET SPACE

The whole universe is a Galaxy bar,
With planets, comets and shooting stars,
You could go on a trip to the Milky Way,
All in one fantastic fabulous day!
Comets are huge Smarties that are floating round,
Crash, when they bang they make a big sound!
Planets are made with wonderful sweets to sell,
Chocolatey sweets and dripping caramel,
Green slimy aliens, and all sorts of fellows,
Come to buy great gooey marshmallows!
The sun is a big lump of delicious rock,
Shooting stars come from bottles of pop,
The whole universe is a Galaxy bar!

Siobhan Gilliam (10)
Canada Hill Primary School

DOLPHINS

Dolphins are nice, dolphins are cool,
Dolphins have fins that are suitable.
Their skin is smooth, their flippers are strong,
They splash and splosh like *ping, pang, pong.*
Dolphins are small, dolphins are tall,
I like them when they are in the pool.
I don't know, do you think they're cool?

Holly Trethewey (11)
Canada Hill Primary School

THE DAY MAIL

This is the day mail crossing the border,
Bringing the cheque and the postal order,
Letters from the old, letters from the young,
Letters from the girl that the train has brung,
Climbing up Beatock, a gradual climb,
No need to hurry 'cause she's on time,
Past cotton, grass and moorland boulder,
Shovelling grey steam over her shoulder,
Finally she's home in the big city,
After one great, great, big, big ditty.

Karl Cheesman (11)
Canada Hill Primary School

THUNDER AND LIGHTNING

Boom, boom starts the storm,
As the lightning starts to form.
As the thunder shakes the sea,
As the lightning strikes the trees.
As the thunder starts to cry,
Then the lightning takes over the sky.
As the thunder does a *bash,*
Then the lightning does a *crash.*
As the thunder goes to bed,
And the lightning's already *dead!*

Ben Gaywood (10)
Canada Hill Primary School

GOLDILOCKS (THE TRUTH!)

Do you know the story of Goldilocks?
It isn't true she had smelly socks!
One day she was taking a walk in the woods,
(For her mother kindly said she could,)

When she came across a dainty little house,
She tiptoed up to it (as quiet as a mouse!)
For Goldy was quite a little lady,
(That isn't true it's just a maybe!)

She went inside and saw lots of porridge,
Her mother once made some (it tasted horrid!)
So she tiptoed up the steep, grey stairs,
In a blue room there was a row of three chairs.

The chair that would fit Goldy was quite low,
It had on it a little blue bow!
But Goldy thought that bows were for babies,
She walked on thinking she was a lady!

She went into a room full of toys,
But all these toys were really only for boys!
Goldy thought that this wasn't really fair,
But she was tired (she didn't care.)

She must have dozed off for about two hours,
('Cause she had, had a dream about flowers!)
She sat up and got out of bed,
And found she had a horribly painful head.

Then she thought she would have to go home.
Plus, the people here were unknown.
Goldy never went back to that dainty little house,
Even when she was as quiet as a mouse!

Sarah Gilbert (10)
Canada Hill Primary School

34

THE VICIOUS SHARK

The shark is a very vicious fish,
It has very sharp teeth like razor blades.

At dinner time the shark gets angry,
Beware don't go swimming in the night,
Crunch.

The shark comes forward, its eyes roll back,
Crunch, crunch and *crunch* as the shark's
teeth grind the flesh.

The shark is a very vicious fish,
It has very sharp teeth like razor blades.

Victoria Smith (11)
Canada Hill Primary School

METEORITES

The meteorites are coming,
They are ruining the Earth.

You can hear their death-defying roar
From the lovely town of 'Lubleth'.

The huge balls of fire
Come crashing through the Earth's atmosphere.

Alex Pugh (10)
Canada Hill Primary School

A Shower Is A Drip Drop

Splashing out spit,
A shower is a fall,
Massive and holey,
A shower is a big foot,
Hairy and spotty,
A shower is a cold spot,
Musty and black,
A shower is a mouldy place,
Spitting out drops,
Showers are a ditch's green spots,
Big and massive.

John David Paddon (11)
Canada Hill Primary School

Elephants, Elephants

Elephant, elephant, how gorgeous you look,
I didn't know that you read books,
Elephant, elephant, please don't charge at me,
Why did you hurt the little bee?
Elephant, elephant, how amazing you are,
I can hear you from very far,
Elephant, elephant, I'm so sorry to leave you,
So long, farewell, bye elephant.

Naomi Richards (11)
Canada Hill Primary School

PIKACHU RAP

Pikachu, Pikachu, he may electrocute you,
I'll watch out incase his brother comes out, Raichu.
Kill him, kill him, Pikachu or else you're stew.
Charmander is out, kill him now, chuck him in the hay.
Here have some super potion Pikachu, OK.
Use a Pokéball to catch Charmander, *yay*.

Ben Sampson (11)
Canada Hill Primary School

JABBERWOCKY

I thought I'd meet you standing here,
I'm afraid to say he's awfully near.

The forests getting darker now,
He'll eat you up just like a cow.

And here he comes, the awful beast,
You'll be a mighty handsome feast!

Oh no, he's coming right for me,
He's got my leg, this cannot be.

But I'm unarmed, it's him you should get,
He thought to himself, oh what a threat.

But it kept on chewing on the old, old man,
So the knight just turned and ran and ran.

Struan Gray (10)
Diptford Parochial Primary School

THE ZOO

It's Sunday, hooray,
I'm off to Paignton Zoo today,
To see the monkeys, lions
And giraffes.

I love to watch the penguins,
When they are being fed, waddling
Around to get a fish,
Slipping and sliding to get into their pool.

I watch the keepers, they've hidden
The elephants food, it's fun to watch but,
The elephants know just where to look,
In five seconds they have eaten the lot.

I love all the animals at the zoo,
I would stay all night if I could.
To hear all the sounds that they make,
Especially the ducks on the lake.

Gemma Preston (10)
Eden Park Junior School

THE BEACH

The sky is clear,
The sea is blue,
Walking alone just me and you.
Making castles in the sand,
Holding pebbles in my hand.
It's nice to live by the sea,
We've got to go it's time for tea.

Joseph Vince (8)
Eden Park Junior School

THE INDIAN CHANT

The chief is watching his servants die,
Because their throats are awfully dry.
The chief has tied his servants to a wall,
So he doesn't have to bother at all.

Powwow, powwow, powwow, powwow,
Powwow, powwow, powwow, powwow.

The eagle swoops high and low,
The Indians come and come to go,
The chief gets angry with his servants,
And they came to serve some more.

Powwow, powwow, powwow, powwow,
Powwow, powwow, powwow, powwow.

Mark Coysh (11)
Eden Park Junior School

MY FAMILY

I've got a dad that's big and strong,
His legs are really, really long.

I've got a mum that's mega soft,
She's too frightened to go into the loft.

I've got a brother that's really cheeky,
When he's in a car he gets really peaky.

I've got a sister that's really shy,
She turns away when people go by.

And now for me, I've got to go to bed,
And snuggle up with Little Ted.

Gemma Harris (9)
Eden Park Junior School

A IS FOR AARDVARK

A is for aardvark who sniffs all night.
B is for bat who gives a nasty bite.
C is for Cleopatra who writes a script.
D is for donkey who lives in Egypt.
E is for elephant who trudges along.
F is for fire bell that gives a big bong.
G is for gorilla who bangs his chest.
H is for hippo, them birds are a pest.
I is for insects, big and small.
J is for judge, who walks through the door.
K is for koala who climbs up a tree.
L is for lemons, where's the bee?
M is for mountains high and tall.
N is for numbers, three and four.
O is for ostrich really high.
P is for pony, another one goes by.
Q is for quail, there's his quilt.
R is for robber, look what he's built.
S is for spaceship up very high.
T is for tiger jumping by.
U is for umbrella keeping you from getting wet.
V is for volcano I'll bet.
W is for William on the phone.
X is for x-ray that shows my bones.
Y is for yo-yo, up and down.
Z is for zebra with a bound.

Thomas Carter (8)
Eden Park Junior School

MY RABBIT

My rabbit's called Casper and he thinks he's a cat
And I really like that
He is really funny
And he is a lovely bunny
He lives in a hutch
And he does not like that very much
He likes it when the sun is out
And he always jumps about
He likes it best when he's indoors with us
And he loves it when we make a fuss
He's got lovely soft ears and big white feet
And carrots are his special treat.

Daisy Caunter (7)
Eden Park Junior School

ANIMAL ANTICS

One old and objectionable owl,
Two troublesome, terrific tigers,
Three thirsty, twittering thrushes,
Four furious, fierce foxes,
Five funny, freckled fish,
Six sliding, slithering snakes,
Seven swooping, swimming seagulls,
Eight enormous, evil elephants,
Nine nibbling nice nightingales,
Ten tender, tiptoeing turtles.

Stephen Bryant (8)
Eden Park Junior School

THE OWL SONG!

Neither mouth nor arms have I
But I catch my prey at night,
And I have
Big eyes, big eyes, big eyes.

Neither diseases nor poisons have I
But I have no hair just feathers,
And I have
Big eyes, big eyes, big eyes.

I master every movement
for I creep up on my prey and eat them,
And I have
Big eyes, big eyes, big eyes.

Chloe-Anne Leonard (10)
Eden Park Junior School

LEMON SPONGE CAKE

I love lemon sponge cake with sugar on top,
I can't get enough of the glorious taste.
I love it when Mum bakes one,
She gives it the right touch.

I wish I could eat it all myself,
It's so delicious for my tummy.
Yummy, yummy, yummy,
I love it, love it, love it.

Dad can't bake,
He only cooks the dinner.
His dinners are yummy,
Yummy, yummy.

Louise Hodson (10)
Eden Park Junior School

FREEDOM COMES FOR THE INDIANS

Arrows flying in the air,
Riot running everywhere,
The beating of drums as loud as can be.

Fire! Fire! Fire! Light!
Fire! Fire! Fire! Light!

Freedom comes for everyone,
To us our brothers have come,
Round the firelight we dance together.

Fire! Fire! Fire! Light!
Fire! Fire! Fire! Light!

We share a feast together,
We have now fought forever,
For we have gained our freedom forever.

Fire! Fire! Fire! Light!
Fire! Fire! Fire! Light!

Sammy Sharpe (10)
Eden Park Junior School

AIR RAID

I could see misty smoke as misty as mist itself.
I could see frightened faces scared that they will die.
I could see a blazing fire as fiery as Hell itself.
I could see people huddled up praying for their lives.
I could feel a shiver of coldness as cold as a winter's morning.
I could feel the vibration of the bombs when they dropped.
I could sense a sense of relief once the bombs had stopped.

Tom Lewis (10)
Eden Park Junior School

SISTERS

When I go to Emma's house,
For she is my best friend
There's just one thing she moans about,
It drives me round the bend,
Her sister.

She moans her sister breaks her toys,
She moans she keeps her awake.
She moans her sister tells of her,
When it was only a mistake.

When I go to Emma's house
And her sister's there instead,
There's just one thing she moans about,
It's all that's in her head,
Her sister.

She moans her sister breaks her toys,
She moans she keeps her awake.
She moans her sister tells of her,
When it was only a mistake.

When people ask which one I don't like,
I have to answer none
For the thing that I don't get is,
Why don't they find each other fun?

Hannah Ellis (10)
Eden Park Junior School

BIG BEN CHIMES AGAIN

Big Ben chimes again,
Hours passing by.
Dong, dong, dong,
Past the hours fly.

One o'clock, two o'clock,
Three o'clock, four,
The tourists are leaving
After their tour.

They have seen
The workings of Ben,
The 'Father of Time',
That they might never see ever again.

Hannah Clyburn (9)
Eden Park Junior School

I SAW

I saw a fox eating a rabbit.
I saw a hippie picking his nose
because that was his habit.
I saw a dog weeing on a brick wall.
I saw an old lady, she had a big fall.
I saw four children going to the fair.
I saw an old man looking at the birds in the air.
I saw a man talking to his mate.
I saw a lady go through the gate.
I saw a policeman in his car.
I saw a little boy opening a chocolate bar.
I saw a baby taking off his nappy.
I saw a little girl very, very happy.

Laura Bond (11)
Eden Park Junior School

THE SPRING THING

Spring, spring, spring,
Oh it's such a wonderful thing.
Delightful daffodils dancing,
And little lambs a-prancing.

The winter season has gone at last!
Spring has sprung upon us so fast!
No more frostbite on our nose,
Or sitting by the fire toasting our toes!

The sun is beaming everywhere,
Birds flying in the fresh spring air.
Everybody has a smile on their face,
As they're pottering around
Spring-cleaning the place!

Joanne Hadley (10)
Eden Park Junior School

PIZZA POEM

The great pizza
The toppings are unending,
Huge, medium or small,
Like the world, big and round,
Like the sea, big and huge.
It makes me feel really excited,
Like a spoilt child that
Everyone ignores,
The great pizza
Stays just for me to eat.

Natalie Dunn (11)
Eden Park Junior School

REBECCA

R   is for me, tall and true
E   is for energy, boundless and endless
B   is for blonde, straight and long
E   is for energetic, endless and flowing
C   is for calm, of which I have none
C   is for caring, which I can be
A   is for anything which I can try

M   is for a mad, crazy girl
A   is for an angel, which I am not
R   is for Rebeccas all over the world
Y   is for you, who puts up with me

L   is for loving, my mum says is me
E   is for an endless loving girl
E   is for everything my mum calls me

Rebecca Lee (9)
Eden Park Junior School

DREAM MACHINES

Computer games are here to stay,
Nintendo, Dreamcast all the way.
There's Banjo, Sonic, Zelda too,
They're all here to play with you.
Platform, sport and racing teams,
Everybody can have these dreams.
Whether it's pads, joysticks, wheels or a gun,
Come on everyone and join in the fun.

Matthew Deakin (9)
Eden Park Junior School

MY MAGIC CARPET

I've got a magic carpet, it'll take me any place,
It'll take me to a shady forest, it'll take me to outer space.
I've been to unknown planets with aliens sweet not scary,
I've been to magical forests, I've even seen a fairy.
I've been to Scotland and seen the Loch Ness monster,
I've been in the coral reef and seen friendly fish and a lobster.

I've been to fantasy chocolate worlds, very nice to eat,
I've been to relaxing beaches with fruit trees, nice and sweet.
I've played with the dolphins and played chase with the whales,
I've chased the lions and even pulled their tails.
I've just been flying over the Millennium Dome,
But now I think it's time to go home.

Siân Sims (9)
Eden Park Junior School

MY SILLY, OLD PUPPY

I've got a puppy short and tubby, always on the go.
She runs like a one-legged frog as she springs into the air.
When she's feeling angry, or wants a good, rough fight,
she grits her teeth as though she's just about to bite.
When she's on the lead, she pulls and drags you along,
everything she sees, she eats!
So when she reaches home she gets a good snack.
When we go in the kitchen, she's left some food on the floor.
I don't know, that's my silly, old puppy.

Sylvia Morrissey (9)
Eden Park Junior School

WITCHCRAFT AND WIZARDRY

As I wandered through the forest at night
I heard a noise which gave me a fright.
As I looked up at the moonlit sky
I saw a figure passing by.
Cackle, cackle in the sky
I saw a witch flying by.
A tree branch behind me snapped.
I shivered, I quivered,
A slimy, pale face came into the light,
I got such a fright.
'Horror, horror,' I cried aloud,
Bats, slugs, snails,
Turn this child oh so pale.
Long bushy beard I see in that shadow,
I shivered, I quivered,
Is it a Black Widow?
Toadstools, fungus, poison ivy.
It was a witch about to cast a spell,
We bless upon the dead,
I break into your head,
Let your scared being
Posses us with a demon seed.

Kesha Ayres (10)
Eden Park Junior School

A Scarecrow Remembers Winter

Early one crisp morning
Just as the day was dawning,
I saw three children who were mourning
That there was no snow.

Then after school, returning fast,
They saw the snow had come at last.
The sad, glum faces now had passed
And smiles shone all around.

The snowy blanket covered the land,
like a beach of sparkly white sand.
The children now had frozen hands
As they began to play.

The snow was rolled into a ball,
It started small but ended tall.
A wonderful time was had by all
Asthey finished the snowman's face.

Joe Tarbuck (11)
Eden Park Junior School

The Surfboarder

Riding the ocean waves,
As fast as I can,
On a surfboard,
A wetsuited man.

Travelling nearer to the sandy shore,
I want to do it forever more!
The shiny board underneath my feet
Has got me feeling really neat!

The rush of adrenaline is really cool
When I crash into a rock pool.
I think I might hear a sonic boom
As I go glidin' into a blue room.

Dancing around on the everlasting waves
Surfing is the pride of my days.
Cool as ice,
Thin as rice,
Is the board of my dreams.

Daniel Clark (10)
Eden Park Junior School

Up, Up And Away

Up, up and away
on a fresh spring day,
all the flowers are sleeping
and the cows are still eating.

Up, up and away
on a hot sunny day,
all the children's laughter
will be remembered for ever after.

Up, up and away
on a rainy, autumn day,
see some people talking
while others are quickly walking.

Up, up and away
on a cold winter's day,
looking down below
at the lovely, white snow.

Daniel Stephen (7)
Eden Park Junior School

THE BEST PLACE TO STAY

You know the best place to stay,
Not at home because I say
Try Tunisia, it's a wonderful place
Where you have plenty of room and space.
The swimming pools are great,
Now that's what I mean, mate!
No need to cook for yourself
There's plenty of room on the shelf.
Whizz down the pool slides as often as you like,
Why don't you perhaps ride a bike.
Go on trips everywhere,
The perfect place to be is there.

Abbie Luscombe (9)
Eden Park Junior School

TEN TEACHERS

Ten teachers in the staff room smoking cigarettes,
Nine teachers locked up in the cupboard scared of the headteacher,
Eight teachers in a car, they don't know what to do,
Seven teachers swigging tea with a slurp,
Six teachers in a chair reading comics with a grin,
Five teachers planning and giving out homework,
Four teachers frightened of the children,
Three teachers worn and tired, sitting in an arm chair,
Two teachers playing chess and scratching their heads while they think,
One teacher going home, how tired she looks.

William Rowe Jones (8)
Eden Park Junior School

THE SOLAR ECLIPSE

The solar eclipse
is a hey-diddle-diddle!
The sun and the Earth
and the moon in the middle.
The sky is very black.
The sun's behind the moon,
but it will get much lighter,
very, very soon.
Now suddenly it's
as light as day,
thank goodness the sun
has not gone away!
The moon's full of craters
and it is quite round,
but it proves there's nothing living
for no water can be found.
No people go there
for the sun is too hot,
wear special clothes, or
you'll get burnt a lot!
The earth has got countries,
yes, countries galore,
and houses with windows,
some roofs and a door.
The sun is too bright
for people to see,
and if you did look,
blind you might be.
Do you get my message?
I hope it hits some.
So please *do* remember,
Don't look at the sun!

Charlotte Trombin (8)
Eden Park Junior School

ON SAFARI

Out on safari one day,
all the animals were at play.

The lions were hunting for food,
their cubs were in a playful mood.
The monkeys swinging from tree to tree
to play and scream, we love to see.

Hippos wallow in pools of mud,
a wash for them needs no soap suds.
On safari with me
would you like to be?

Rebecca Stone (8)
Eden Park Junior School

A RAINY DAY

Grey clouds, *pitter-patter*
goes the heavy rain.
Puddles, water, spitting down,
like golden droplets of rain.
I stay inside the house
and watch the roaring rain,
I wish I could go out to play
on a very sunny day.
Up goes my umbrella,
open I the door, I step outside
with my anorak on
and walk into a watery tide.

Adam James (11)
Eden Park Junior School

SCHOOL DINNERS

I hate school dinners,
they drive me round the bend,
especially the mushy peas,
they don't let me sit with a friend.

At Christmas the potatoes are mouldy,
they are very green.
I hate cabbage very much,
which I wish I'd never seen.

For drinks, they give you water,
for dessert they give you custard,
the sprouts are green and horrid
and everything gets covered in mustard.

They give you pizza
with green chilli on top,
the tomatoes get covered in ketchup.
You get detention if you ask for pop!

So we nagged and nagged the dinner ladies
to give us a nicer meal,
and we have jam roly-poly now
and they promise to keep it a deal!

Charlotte Bower (9)
Eden Park Junior School

THE WORM

I am a worm,
I am pink and wriggly
and I squirm.

I spend so much time on my belly
that I never get round to
watching the telly.

I love to come out in the rain
and in the soil
I dig like a train.

Some birds think that I am yummy,
so my friends usually
end up in their tummy.

Laura Duncan (11)
Eden Park Junior School

MP

Damn you Mr Politician!
You're in a very cushy position,
Your word is law,
But your decisions are poor.
Remember my friend,
You'll come to a sticky end.
Pride comes before a fall.
You had power, but misused it all.
Just wait until the next election,
There's got to be a better selection,
Than you.

Adam Yersin (11)
Eden Park Junior School

THE INDIAN DRUM

The Indians come to drum away,
for another holiday.
They dance around the fire
to greet their Sire.

We come again
to meet again,

Drum-a, drum-a, drum-a, drum-a-drum.
Drum-a, drum-a, drum-a, drum-a-drum.

The white men come to take our village
and our knowledge,
then they go with our gold
for the old.

We come again
to meet again,

Drum-a, drum-a, drum-a, drum-a-drum.
Drum-a, drum-a, drum-a, drum-a-drum.

They kill our brothers with a gun
for their fun.
They take away our Sire
and blow out the fire.

We come again
to meet again,

Drum-a, drum-a, drum-a, drum-a-drum.
Drum-a, drum-a, drum-a, drum-a-drum.

Donna Walsh (11)
Eden Park Junior School

ANIMALS OF THE WORLD

Monkeys jump from tree to tree,
Dolphins live deep in the sea,
Lions lay soft on their backs,
Mice live in a haystack,
Snakes slither over the rocks,
Sheep wander around in flocks,
Giraffes eat twigs and leaves,
Cats do as they please,
Rabbits live in a hutch,
Skunks smell - I don't like them much!

Brittany Caunter (9)
Eden Park Junior School

THE CHEBRAH

The Chebrah has big, beady eyes,
His skin is black with yellow stripes
And on that skin, black spots are there,
Because he's a cross between a cheetah and zebra.
He runs very fast, and poison he breathes.
His claws, very sharp,
That reach down to his knees.
He lives on Cripton, planet of weather,
Along with Suk, Gem and Gindelizer.

Kieran James (11)
Eden Park Junior School

WHAT THE SCARECROW SAW

'Head of straw and heart of wood,
With arms outstretched like I've stood
For half a year in Hertfordshire,
My feet stuck in the mud.' (by Colin West)

Things could be worse for I remember
One day in late December,
Look!
The children came running up,
Wheeling a rusty, creaky barrow,
Filled with crisp, white snow.
Do you know what they were doing?
Building a snowman!

The children were wearing
A coat like sheepskin,
Holly berry hats,
Red cheeks,
Rudolph red noses,
Their toes were like blocks of ice.
They scooped up handfuls of snow.
First a body, then a head,
Some raisins for its eyes,
Coal for buttons,
A scarf wrapped gently around him.

I looked across the field,
It was like the North Pole.
In the morning as I woke up, he'd melted.
The sun had got him.

Hannah Caunter (10)
Eden Park Junior School

HARRY POTTER'S ADVENTURES

Harry Potter, wizard at birth
Got his lightning scar from a curse.
Grew up with Muggles,
Not knowing his past,
When he found out what he was at last
A famous wizard at the best wizard school,
Hogwarts!
Where he meets his new best friends;
Ron Weasley overshadowed by his many brothers
And Hermionie Granger clever, sensible and kind.
As the year closed to an end
Harry defeats Lord Voldemort again
Saving that stone that gives forever life,
Wins the house cup for Griffindor.
Harry goes back to the Muggle life
Will he ever see his friends again,
When, how?
In two months time he'll be back at Hogwarts,
His real home.

Mikaela Boarer (11)
Eden Park Junior School

WHALES AND DOLPHINS

Whales and dolphins, so sparkly and nice,
They jump so high and make a big splash.
They spend most of their time under the water,
But when they are on the surface, they are a lot of fun.
They make a lot of noise on the surface
And under the water.

Annabel Mitchell (9)
Eden Park Junior School

THE STAR

The little star shines in the night,
Lighting everything that isn't bright.
When the sun finally goes down,
Stars glow in a little town.
In the little town there isn't a peep,
Because everyone is now asleep.
But no, a man called Mr Rake
Is still lying there awake.
The little star twinkles in the moonlight,
Then goes down and appears next night.

Now it's time to go to sleep,
The little town hears no peep.
Finally Mr Rake rests his head,
In his cosy, sleep-warming little bed.
Finally Mr Rake goes to sleep,
But somewhere else there is a beep.
A little boy called Davy Jones
Is feeding his puppy dog Bones.
His mother shouts 'Go to sleep.'
And once again, there isn't a peep.

Max Pontin (10)
Eden Park Junior School

AIR RAIDS

I saw light from the bombs,
I heard planes swooping in for attack,
I smelt smoke from the fires,
Then I felt relief.

Zack Bevan (11)
Eden Park Junior School

A SCARECROW REMEMBERS

'Head of straw and heart of wood
With arms outstretched like I've stood
For half a year in Hertfordshire,
My feet stuck in the mud.' (by Colin West)

Things could be worse for I remember
One day in late December,

It was all cold
Like summer had been sold,
The crispy white snow
For children to throw,
They build a snowman
Who is my brother.
They use stones for his eyes,
So he's not like another,
A carrot for his nose,
His mouth made of hose.

The sun came out, he melted away,
But by next December
He will be back to play.

So with arms outstretched,
I stand alone for half a year
In *Hertfordshire.*

Cara Hendriksen (11)
Eden Park Junior School

WEEPING WILLOW

Weeping willow with tears running down,
Why do you always weep and frown?
Sobbing, crying, frowning too,
Weeping willow do you really have to?
Laughing willow, giggling with glee,
Now you are more like me.
It's better to be happy,
To let your leaves fall softly,
Be a laughing, not a weeping willow.

Rebekah Glanvill (9)
Eden Park Junior School

THE GIRL (OTHERWISE KNOWN AS CINDERELLA)

All alone and dressed in rags,
a little girls with carrier bags.
Her eyes are green and extremely tiny,
her neck is thin and very spiney.
Her body is neglected
and her soul is rejected.
She probably has a heart of gold,
but there's many ways this story can be told.
She has to work every hour
her dwelling is a mouse-infested tower.
She also has a stepmum and two sisters,
who are fat and have red blisters.
She cooks for them and feeds
while the other two do evil deeds,
and just to put you to the test,
I'm not going to tell you the rest.

Matthew Hale (11)
Exeter Cathedral School

LOVE

Out from a gentle heart comes love,
Swiftly, graceful as a dove.
In and out within a grove,
Precious as a treasure trove.
Flowers grow within, without,
A fairy flutters all about.
Then the silent pair appear,
The vision is becoming clear.
In secret together they shall meet,
The sound of love is so sweet.
Out from their gentle hearts comes love,
Swiftly, graceful as a dove.

Catriona Rodger (9)
Exeter Cathedral School

SPACE

Space is a peaceful, empty place,
Silver twinkling stars above.
The sun is so big, you can't fit your arms round it,
You wouldn't dare, it's so very burning hot.
Space is dark and gloomy,
The planets are rather colourful,
Jupiter is so very bright, as the sun,
The sun is yellow and orange.
Space is opening up to the heavens.

Jessica Wood (9)
Exeter Cathedral School

HOMEWORK SESSION!

From a devil's point of view:

> Every night we scamp upstairs
> And loudly pull out all the chairs,
> If someone tries to tell us off,
> We just say, 'Oh, what a boff!'

From an angel's point of view:

> Every night we creep upstairs
> And quietly pull out the rest of the chairs.
> We are too good to be told off,
> And do not like being called a boff.

From a teacher's point of view:

> Some are good and some are bad,
> Some just totally drive me mad,
> Some are loud and some are silent
> And some are positively violent!

Rebecca Westley (11)
Exeter Cathedral School

SPACE

Space is dark and mysterious and frightening,
There are fiery comets passing at the speed of light.
Some people say that it opens up to the heavens.
When astronauts go up in space they say, 'Why, it's so peaceful.'
Then the astronauts say, 'Look at all the fabulous stars,

> aren't they bright?'

Ashleigh-Jade Black (8)
Exeter Cathedral School

THE NEW CENTURY

A brand new century has come to call,
Health and happiness to one and all.
Bring on the fireworks and all the fun,
Keep the party going till 2001!

People celebrate all over the Earth,
Now is the time of Christ's great birth.
There wasn't much snow in '99,
But the sooner the cold's gone, the sun will shine.

Let's hope that in this happy year
There will be nothing for anyone to fear.
Just be joyful and full of gladness,
There will be no bad or any sadness.

Everyone shouted when Big Ben struck midnight,
And the fireworks, wow, what a sight!
Peace to everyone and everything,
Parties and fun while the bells ring!

Lara-Clare Bourdeaux (10)
Exeter Cathedral School

SCIENCE

Today is Wednesday, I am off to the lab.
Science is fun, never drab.
Will it be wires, worms or volts?
No, it's thunder and lightning bolts.
Oh Miss Thomas, we think you are nice,
After the hols, can I dissect the mice?

Daniel Jones (10)
Exeter Cathedral School

GIRLS

The girl who sits on the bench over there,
Is really nice but has weird hair.
She's nice and sweet
Like little Bo Peep,
But has curls instead of straight hair.

It's a pity she's come to cry,
I said to her, 'Why don't you try?
Why don't you try to smile once more.
We don't want your tears to make it pour.'

She's probably got a heart of gold,
But it's got broken in the cold.
Oh how I love that girl so dear,
My love to her is like a swirl.

Freddy Barnes (10)
Exeter Cathedral School

A HUNGRY LION

Have you ever seen a lion looking at her prey,
watching in the long, dry grass?
Suddenly she pounces at her very startled lunch.
The antelope that she has caught tries to get away,
but the lion is too strong and kills the poor creature
with one, big scratch.
Next, she roars to get the other lions.
Over the plains they come to enjoy a feast
that has been prepared.

Naomi Sourbut (9)
Exeter Cathedral School

SPACE

Space has planets big and small,
Space has the sun burning like a great gas ball.
Space has lots of stars shining bright,
Hanging in the sky at night.
Space is mysterious and dark,
Like night-time in the park.
Space is magnificent and vast,
Space has comets going very fast.

Sean Flynn (8)
Exeter Cathedral School

SPACE

Space, it's a mysterious place.
Its burning sun and its shooting stars,
Flying asteroids, galaxies which open up to the heavens,
An overwhelming number of stars that twinkle,
Like little lights.

Archie Miller (9)
Exeter Cathedral School

SPACE

Space is a mysterious place,
Twinkling stars as the moonlight shines,
Dashing asteroids here and there,
The burning sun hotter than anything in space.
The cold, spooky quietness of the dark night of space.

Thomas Rainey (8)
Exeter Cathedral School

SPEED OF TIME

I have heard of many lies
Over my short childhood's time,
When of life's end someone dies
Life and death is in the vine.

Like a kingfisher's dive, life swiftly flows,
Piercing turquoise of our days,
Deepening death harshly blows,
Saddening in a bewildering maze.

The dead body may go down the drove,
Not found on the silentest, darkest night
To where the rushing river clove,
But finding the full moon of hopeful delight.

Camilla Biggs (8)
Exeter Cathedral School

SPACE

I wish I could touch all the stars,
I wish I could land on Mars.
Hurtling comets and whizzing probes,
I wish I could land on one of those.
Spooky darkness and blazing fire,
I wonder when the world will tire
Of going round and round the sun.
I wonder if we'll find another one?

Tobi Herpoldt McCrone (8)
Exeter Cathedral School

SPACE

Space is magnificent, it is the opening of the heavens.
There are comets circling, there are comets hurtling.
Space is hot and cold, space is really bold.
Thunder, like the speed of light, gleaming stars all twinkling bright.
In space it is really silent, the sun's heat is really violent.
Space is really interesting.

Aurora Moxon (8)
Exeter Cathedral School

NIBBLES

Whiskers twitching, bright little eyes
Fur as soft as snow.
Round and round on her wheel she flies,
Always fast, never slow.

She curls in a ball all day
And snoozes until it's night,
Then, she comes out to play
Whilst the stars and moon are bright.

Food is carried in her pouch
To store for a later time,
Then she plays with me on the couch
And there's nothing she can't climb.

I love her more than any toy,
She gives me lots of joy.
We're always together after tea,
My sweet little hamster, Nibbles, and me.

Katy Cooper (8)
Greylands Prep School

CATS

Cats are mysterious animals
because you never know
what they are thinking.

Emerald eyes, velvet fur,
sharp claws and
tails for balancing.

Mice to eat, meat to chew,
fur for cleaning,
milk for drinking.

But you know,
she's your boss.

Michael Tucker (9)
Greylands Prep School

MY GUINEA PIG, BRIAN

He has long hair
And a cute button nose.
He is black, brown and white
With little hairy toes.
Brian is chubby
But he is not very big.
He is my funny pet,
My guinea pig.

Joshua Mason (7)
Greylands Prep School

POLAR BEAR CUBS

Polar bears creep up in the clear, white snow.
No one sees them, no one knows.
Blending into the clear, white snow,
polar bears are walking and no one knows.
Polar bear cubs looking for their mum,
little tiny polar bears with rumbling tums.

Sally Pickering (8)
Greylands Prep School

MY RABBIT

My rabbit is grey and furry.
My rabbit is fast and eats grass,
She lives in a hutch
And she likes a carrot for lunch.
She sleeps in the hay and when
It is sunny, she comes out to play.

James Parish (8)
Greylands Prep School

CHEETAH POEM

The cheetah swishes in the grass,
faster he goes,
for it is his prey.
He gets it suddenly,
he eats it,
he runs away.

William Perrett (8)
Greylands Prep School

MY HEDGEHOG

My hedgehog has spiky spines.
He's very small
And he's a real porcupine.
He's got a twitchy nose.

He lives under our shed
And eats slimy, sloppy cat food.
He has a tiny head
And eats creepy, crawly slithery slugs.

He's a stumpy, slow hedgehog,
And he's got glowing eyes.
He climbs on a big, old, mossy log,
And he's not noisy at all.

Kathryn Morris (8)
Greylands Prep School

PENNY'S TAIL

Penny is an old dog, but she thinks she is a puppy,
Because she plays all day and runs away,
I think she is lucky.
She always wants crisps and crumbs that have
Fallen off the kitchen table.
She would eat our sweets if she were able.

Cara Duerden (7)
Greylands Prep School

MY FAVOURITE SMILE

Kathryn and Sally have nice smiles,
So do Jasmin and Paul.
Annabel Brown has a horrible one
Cos she doesn't like me at all.
George and Jack's are okay I suppose
And Ben doesn't smile at all.
Ollie and Danny have weird smiles
And Anne only smiles at The Mall.
But when I go home in time for tea
My mum is there with a great big,
Huge,
Ginormous
Smile
For me!

Rebecca Hadley (9)
Greylands Prep School

FYFE THE HORSE

Fyfe the horse, he loves to graze on green grass.
He gallops away so graceful and fast.
He sleeps in a stable in a yard,
In shows he tries very hard.
All the champions race him,
Compared to my horse, they're very slim.
He's cute, he's cuddly, he's very kind.
When he's in a field, he's hard to find.

George Harris (9)
Greylands Prep School

MY DOG

My dog is a mess
and more like the opposite
of a success.
She is black with a patch of white.
She wakes up and moans
in the night.
She has smooth fur
and she hates it when
the cat goes 'purr'.
She walks similar to a hawk
but with four legs.
She has a big, warm den with
a little teddy bear
called Ben.

Daniel Vaughton (9)
Greylands Prep School

BOOBOO!

My cat is
The world's best cat.
She's so funny,
I love her as much as I can,
Booboo.

Not fat,
Ordinary.
The whole village knows her,
She goes next door and eats their food,
Content!

Kallie Johnson (10)
Hennock Community Primary School

THE CAT KING

My cat walks like a superstar,
He'd love a car
And a bar
And a spa.
He's so fast at running
And very cunning,
And stunning.
He's the Leonardo of the cat world.
He brings girl cats home.
He always gives you that look,
'Don't put me outside.'
I sighed,
He cried.
He knows I love him,
But does he love me?

Joanna Newton (11)
Hennock Community Primary School

SMOKY, MY CAT

Smoky,
He's so fluffy,
He is the cutest thing.
He is my only cat,
Smoky.
He's so alive,
He likes taking things.
He is the funniest yet,
Smoky.

Christine Seward (9)
Hennock Community Primary School

Jo

My budgie Jo is very lively.
When you go and put your finger in the cage,
Jo will bite you.
When he wants some food,
Jo eats it from the floor of the cage.
When you put your fist at the bottom of the cage,
He will follow it.
He is very clever!

Rachel Martin (9)
Hennock Community Primary School

In Joe's Head

In Joe's head are some beautiful girls,
But the rest is just football, football and
                                    more football,
And a little space for his pets.

Henry Harvey (9)
Hennock Community Primary School

Flowers

In the grassy wood,
Some wonderful flowers stood.
I wonder if I could play among the flowers every day?
On the 31st of May the flowers come out to play,
I wish I could stay and play nearly every day.

Alexander Hayden (9)
Manor House School

MY MODEL RAILWAY

In the loft stands a model railway
On which I like to play.
I've built stations, signal boxes, houses and shops
To keep me amused all day.
The hills are made from plaster and wire
And painted green and brown,
The roads are painted in dark grey
To give me a little town.
I operate the trains from a control box
Which is connected to the track.
The diesel leaves Whimple at ten o'clock
And thirty seconds later it's back.

Paul Holborow (11)
Manor House School

BIRD WATCHING

I watch the birds up in the sky,
Watch them soaring, see them fly,
As they wash their tiny wings,
Hear the pretty song they sing.
Listen to the glorious tone,
Never do you hear them moan.

The robin with his red breast bold,
The great tit with his blue and gold,
The woodpecker in the old oak tree,
I hear him, but he doesn't see me.

Sophie Collett (10)
Manor House School

I LIKE LUNCH

I like lunch.
It could be mash or crunch,
Oh how I like to munch
My lunch.

Sharon is our cook,
She doesn't need a book.
She just makes delicious meals
Just about on wheels.

Every day after play,
I eat my lunch straight away.
It is so yummy
In my tummy.
I like lunch.

James Horman (8)
Manor House School

CARS

Cars, cars and automobiles
From piston rods to dirty wheels.
There are old cars and new cars
And cars in between.
There are big cars and small cars
And cars you've never seen.
Lorries with loads
On first class roads
And if you can't read the signs
You'll be getting massive fines.
At the end of the day the cars come home,
They park in the garage, all alone.

Ben Matthews (9)
Manor House School

PAINTING

Painting is fun,
Painting is great,
I mix the paint up
In one little plate.
I put it in pots
and it makes Mummy cross.

I set to work
making a picture
Out of paint
and Mum is always alert.
I was painting a picture
of a saint,
Mum took one look
and started to faint,
So I didn't do any more
Painting!

Amy Channing (8)
Manor House School

VEHICLES

My daddy's van is very old
and it doesn't really like the cold.
The body work is bound to rust,
it would not be good to make a bus.
A new van is coming soon,
but not until after noon.
Although the van is at its end,
it's still my very best friend.

Rupert Perry (8)
Manor House School

SPRING

I am glad that spring is here,
It means that my birthday's near.
The early daffodils are looking gay
And in the breeze they start to sway.
The days are longer the sun is near,
I am glad it's a new year.

My Mum is glad that spring is here,
Because the sky is very clear,
So she can grow her flowers and veg
And snowdrops start to grow in the hedge.

So that is why we are glad you see,
Next, the summer is going to be.
Bright and sunny it will be,
With all the boats bobbing down at the quay.

Phillippa Frost (10)
Manor House School

WINTER IN THE COUNTRY

The trees are blowing left and right,
The cat's green eyes are alight.
The leaves are floating on the breeze
The children's hands are going to freeze.

The horses are cantering to and fro,
Across the field covered in snow.
The badgers have caught the winter's cold,
The sheep are safe in their warm, grass fold.

Harriet Carr (8)
Manor House School

BUGS

Creepy, crawly,
Slow and fast
Hairy, scary bugs run past.
Squishy, squashy
Wiggly worms,
Caterpillars crawling, eating ferns.
Ants like soldiers
March in a line,
Taking bits of twigs and twine.
Butterflies that flutter by
Dance like ballerinas in the sky.
Smelly flies with lots of eyes,
Big and small, they're every size.
Bugs of all shapes and form
Will still be here when we're all gone.

BJ Man (8)
Manor House School

MY JOURNEY TO SCHOOL

Tatty houses, muddy roads,
dirty hedges, frogs and toads.
Lollipop lady saying 'Hello'
people walking to and fro.
Spar's are opening, lights are on,
children rushing with coats on.
My mother's waving,
but it won't be long until
the bell goes and I have gone.

Daniel Rowe (10)
Manor House School

TIME

What is time?
As I listen to the chime of the hallway clock,
Tick-tock, tick-tock, tick-tock . . .
Where did it come from? Where is it going?
It doesn't stop, just keeps on flowing,
Tick-tock, tick-tock, tick-tock . . .
All that we do in reason or rhyme will take its
Place in the passage of time.
Tick-tock, tick-tock, tick-tock . . .

Have I lived for a decade, or lived for an hour?
The answer's to be found in time's great power.
Tick-tock, tick-tock, tick-tock . . .
Are we moving forward, or can time stand still?
Tick-tock, tick-tock, tick-tock . . .
Can time move backwards and smooth well-worn hills?
Tick-tock, tick-tock, tick-tock . . .
Is our life in our future, or is it in our past?
Do we stop to think because time moves so fast?
Tick-tock, tick-tock, tick-tock . . .

Laura Young (10)
Manor House School

THE RIVER

River, river, running around,
Whirling and curling going upside down,
Flowing, glowing all around,
Running fast, running slow,
Swishing and curling its path.

Ben Brown
Manor House School

WITCH

The wicked witch with her hat and broom
around the forest she did zoom
looking for ingredients for her spell,
a rat, a toad and a frog's leg as well.
Her dark, black cat was with her too,
looking out for them while she flew.
She changed her spells as she went along,
but most of them always went wrong.
'Flickety flicks and clickety clicks,
I shall turn that man into Weetabix.'
She lived in a house on top of a tree,
where she sometimes invited the wizard to tea.
Nobody had much to fear from her
and sometimes people could hear her cat purr.

Sam Lockwood (9)
Manor House School

MY CRAZY CROCODILE!

I have a crazy crocodile,
His eyes are two pork pies!
He's pink with yellow feathers
And loves to eat ice-cream!
He walks upon the ceiling
And gets around by leaping!
He wears all my dresses when I'm at school,
He likes to ride my bicycle.
I think he's pretty cool!

Hannah Sweet (10)
Manor House School

MOUNTAIN

Tall mountain shrouded in mist,
Craggy head touching the sky,
Nothing to do but stand all day,
Watching the clouds roll by.

Mountaineers with ropes and tents
Climb at frantic pace.
The mountain gazes at their toil,
A smile upon its face.
When they finally reach the top,
They think they've conquered all,
But to the giant watching them,
They still seem very small.

Michael Yaskin (11)
Manor House School

THROUGH THE SKY

I am here up in the sky,
looking down on the fields below.
The people so small, running back and forth,
through the rays of the scorching sun,
then I think how lucky I am
up here in the sky.
But as the day goes on,
I have to land and all is gone.

Ciaran Feeney (10)
Manor House School

THE TIGER

Tiger creeping through the grass
Sees its prey, teeth are bare.
Takes a pounce but is not quick enough
The deer leaps away
Leaving the tiger trying to catch its breath.

Tiger creeping through the grass
Sees its prey, teeth are bare.
Takes a pounce and succeeds.
The deer is lying on the ground,
Vultures, eagles circling round
Trying to have a share.

Katya Moore (9)
Manor House School

LONELINESS

Some people are very lonely
And really wish, if only
They had a friend to play a game,
Then their life wouldn't be such a shame.

They need someone to pair up with in PE
And people to go to their house for tea,
If they had someone to sit next to at dinner time,
Then their life would be just fine.

Alex Hasell (9)
Manor House School

SEASONS FROM MY WINDOW

From my window I can see the start of a wonderful winter.
The snow lies white and bright and good enough to bite.
It lies like icing on a new-made cake.
The trees are capped with white and the houses wrapped in white,
Like feathers on a beautiful swan.

From my window I can see the start of a lovely spring.
The spring brings birds that sing and
Bees that buzz around the foxgloves' buds.

From my window I can see the glorious summer, with all its jewels.
Butterflies, birds and flowers too.
The bright blue sky where the swallows fly.

From my window I can see all the colours of the autumntime.
There's gold and red, brown and orange, not on the trees
But on the ground.

As the seasons rush by and the years disappear,
I realise how different each season is,
But each one is wonderful in so many ways.

Heather Moore (10)
Manor House School

WHAT IS RED?

Red is a shining red shirt, keeping me warm.
Red is a ruby. Red is molten lava
Falling down the sides of a volcano.
A pair of red Wellingtons
Shining with rain.

Charles Coundley (10)
Manor House School

THE MENAGERIE

Our house is full of little feet,
a happier bunch you'll never meet.
Two dogs, two cats and children three,
my dad calls us his menagerie.

The cats, their names are Bonnie and Clyde,
atop our fridge they do reside.
Upon this perch they lie all day,
away from the dogs who want to play.

The dogs, their names are Kelly and Joss,
and my, they like a lot of fuss.
Joss is a baby, only seven weeks old,
but you wouldn't believe it, she's ever so bold.

Kelly is big, boisterous and rough,
but even she sometimes has enough.
Beside the Aga she loves to sleep,
twitching all over as she dreams of sheep.

The children are aged 11, 9 and 5,
Dad often wonders how we'll survive.
It's just a matter of time you see,
till another enters Dad's menagerie.

Nicholas Manning (11)
Manor House School

THE SAILING SHIP

I have a dream
When I am sleeping,
It's a seaside scene,
White horses leaping.

The sea is rough,
The wind is howling,
My Dad's had enough,
The puppy is growling.

But I want to stay
Here on the beach.
On the sand I play,
While seagulls screech.

As I look out to sea,
I spy a ship in sail,
The people on board wave to me,
Suddenly it starts to hail.

The weather gets worse and worse,
The ship begins to rock and roll,
Towards the rocks it takes its course,
'Oh no,' I cry with heart and soul.

I scream and shout and jump around,
I really worry for their plight,
Into my room my Mum must bound,
'Wake up, wake up, Kate, it's alright.'

Katharine Manning (9)
Manor House School

THE HORSE

The horse looked out of his stable
and thought 'If only I was able
to run in the race -
that would be really ace'

I would run like a deer,
the people would cheer
then I would be a hero
just like my name, Nero

I would have much fame
if I joined the game.
I would be top of the table
with my mate, Mabel!

Ginny Baker (8)
Manor House School

THE EAGLE

I love to wander in the hills
and walk among the woods below,
and sometimes when I tire of that
I lie beneath a shady tree and dream,
and fancy in my dreams that I can fly.
I'd soar high and straight above the world,
I'd be an eagle and for a while
golden lord of all the sky.

Katherine Lachlan (10)
Manor House School

MILLENNIUM BUG

It's affecting the computers,
As well as the clocks.
They both think it's the year 1900
So, shoo Millennium Bug, shoo.
We don't want you here any more.

When we want to know the date on our new watch,
It turns out to be 1900.
It's going all around the world
And we want it to stop.
But it won't until next year,
The year 2001.

Everything will be back to normal
As if nothing ever happened.
Let's hope he doesn't come again
Until the year 3000!

Jaycee Crosby (8)
Manor Primary School

SCHOOL'S OUT

School's out, school's out, now it's time for us to shout.
Teachers smell teachers stink, now we don't have time to think.
Dogs are barking, cats do cry, now we're out it's time to fly.
We don't care if we are bad, picking on our mum and dad.
School's out, school's out, now we really are tired out!

Symon Skelly (8)
Manor Primary School

WAR

This ochre-tinged photo,
Showing time, frozen,
Taken by me two decades ago,
A decade after,
Only one was alive.

The most kills, scored in bomb raids,
The blazing fires, the crumbling flats,
Cries of agony, crushed shelters,
War has broken out.
A General assassinated,
Confusion.

Helping injured, shot blindly,
Deadly food, explosions.
Living death,
Mouths frothing blood,
Survivors silent,
Upset, but silent.

Matthew Allen (10)
Manor Primary School

SWEETS

Sugar and spice and all things nice,
Lovely sweets like sugar mice,
A big round sunstopper hanging in the sky,
The lovely sky mix dangling from up high,

Children with dollies,
Making them suck lollies,
Shoelaces come undone,
Then out comes the bubblegum.

Girls taking paces,
While sucking liquorice laces,
Big fat cats,
Eating chocolate rats.

Girls are playing with their hair,
While sucking on a gummie bear,
Boys walk round sucking their thumbs,
Adults sit down,
Chewing on wine gums.

Little boys full of greed,
Are munching on some aniseed,
Some great adult big and tall,
Is choking on a fire ball.

An adult is drinking from a mug,
And at the bottom finds a mint humbug,
A little puppy called Herbert,
Is sucking on some sherbet.

Lauren Weston & Kerri Lugger (9) & Katie Stannard (10)
Manor Primary School

THE MERMAID

I saw a mermaid pale and fair,
Combing down her golden hair,
She swam beneath the sea so blue,
I wish I was a mermaid too,
I would follow her into the sea,
And ask if she would show to me
The place where all the dolphins play,
So I could join them there one day.
I know that this would never be,
But wishing always pleases me.

Katie Stannard (10)
Manor Primary School

I WAS HERE FIRST

'I want to play the PlayStation'
  'I was here first'
'I want to watch the television'
  'I was here first'
'Dad said I could'
  'I was here first'
'Mum says we must share'
  'I was here first'
'Go to your room'
  'I was here first'
'I'm the eldest brother'
  'I was here first.'

Alex Wicks (11)
Marpool Primary School

IF I HAD . . .

If I had . . . a pet *crocodile!*
I could rob a bank in style.
If I had . . . a pet *tiger!*
I could scare everyone and I would be a thriver.
If I had . . . a pet *grizzly bear!*
I could steal rubies rare.
If I had . . . a pet *eagle!*
Wait a second this is all illegal!
But all I've got is a pet mouse!
And all he does is laze in his house.

Samuel Williams (11)
Marpool Primary School

GHOST

When the Earth was young
And the trees were new,
On a deep and crispy night
When the sky was black
And the moon shone bright,
A headless rider came by.
Over the misty hills he rode
To find the love he lost, long ago.
His love was brave and beautiful,
With long, black, flowing hair.
She swore he was at the inn
The night the murder took place.
That night,
So many, many moons ago.

Naomi Hanson (9)
Newport Community School

ALIENS

Aliens are really freaky,
But are they really true?
They can be small and grey, or big and black,
But are they really true?
They swoop down in their alien ships,
But are they really true?
Who knows?

Do they abduct people?
Are they good or bad?
Are they planning to take over the world?
Are they really true?
Who knows?

Do they experiment, and investigate humans?
Do they have big eyes?
Do they have skinny, lank bodies?
Who really knows?

The truth is out there!

Ben Miller (10)
Newport Community School

MY CAT

I have a cat that is so smelly
That rolls around on his belly
He climbs up trees,
He chases the bees,
He has green eyes,
I'll be sad when he dies,
And he sometimes watches the telly!

David Taylor (10)
Newport Community School

CLOSED DOOR - OPEN DOOR

Closed Door

Passage breaker
Wind blocker
Cold stopper
Safety keeper
Room shutter
Handle holder
Cupboard closer
Sound blocker
Light stopper

Open Door

Way opener
Cool maker
Welcome inner
Sunshine letter
Fresh air blower
Journey sender
Surprise shower
Let goer
Jump througher.

Jimmy Sykes (10)
Newport Community School

I LIVE IN A WORLD

I live in a world
Where the sky is blue;
Where birds fly freely
So clear and true.

I live in a world
Where the sun shines bright,
It gives us warmth
And it gives us light.

I live in a world
Where there's a lot of greens;
Lovely trees and grass
For miles can be seen.

I live in a world -
A world of beautiful things.

Fahad Shah (9)
Newport Community School

ICE

It lies there, motionless, on the grass
Like tiny fragments of broken glass.

The ice on the ponds stop the fish from feeding;
While cold damp air on my face, like ice, is freezing.

Melting in patterns as animals pass;
Showing, beneath it, the fresh green grass.

Like mist on the window it clouds our view;
If it hadn't been this cold it would have been dew.

Amanda Verrall (11)
Newport Community School

CREATURES OF THE NIGHT

Green and slimy rust and grimy,
Stone cold gravestone moving behind me,
Slowly approaching with burning thoughts,
When from the grass rose a corpse!

More and more of them seem to come
Answering the calls of the lonely one,
Rising from their forgotten graves
I even saw some Indian braves!

I ran back to the dingy dark wood
I did something bad (anyone could),
I tripped on a vine, fell flat on my face
That's when a man came over with an old suitcase.

As he came nearer I opened my eyes,
His suitcase was full of medical supplies!
He fixed my wounds with bright pink foam,
He gave me a warning but I just ran home.

I was shocked to find (when I was watching the news)
Out of my grazes came very thick ooze,
It looked like it was alive and had nowhere to go
Except for spreading over me from my head to my toe!

Then the next thing happened, I turned very smelly
A wandering monster that stank of flesh and looked like jelly,
But then it went fuzzy like a TV hiccup
That is the point when I woke up.

Matthew Windsor (10)
Newport Community School

LOVE

Love is here
Love is there
Love is everywhere.

You can't hold love
But you can give love
Love makes some people shed a tear.

Love can bring peace and happiness.
Love can make you do silly things
Love can make you go weak at the knees.

You can love people in different ways.
Love is special
You don't have to pay for it
You can give it
And hope for love to come to you.

We need to have love
It is important to everyone
Love could bring joy, hope and happiness.

We love to have love.

Kayleigh Andrews (10)
Newport Community School

THE SWIMMING GALA

It was my turn to race
And I had a pale face;
I stepped up onto the block.
The starter told us to take our marks
And I had a shock,
He had shot the gun to tell us to go,
I dived in and started slow.

I started to speed up,
I had to make my hands the shape of a cup;
I was speeding like a jet
Through the water's net,
Having fun as I went,
It's good there were spare goggles to be lent.

I hit the wall and tumble-turned,
As I pushed off my muscles burned;
I was coming to the half-way mark
And I heard my trainer bark,
'Come on, Hannah, do your best
You can beat all the rest!

Hurry, hurry, as you go,
Don't let aching muscles show.'
I came to the finish and whacked the side,
I thought it may have been a tie
They checked the times, and I had come first!
I am so happy, I think I could burst.

Hannah Pert (11)
Newport Community School

THE RUNNING RACE

Bang, bang, bang
Goes the gun, gun, gun
And run, run, run
Go the men, men, men
And cheer, cheer, cheer
Go the crowd, crowd, crowd
And run, run, run
It's for fun, fun, fun
And they're going, going, going
For the line, line, line
And yes, yes, yes
He's won, won, won!

They're all standing at the line
And waiting to start with the gun
It's the dads' race at sports day
And my dad's won!

Peter Hill (9)
Newport Community School

THE SUN

A bright light
A yellow football
A light giver
A golden candle
An orange star
A bronze clock
A ball of fire.

Laura Baglow (10)
Newport Community School

What A Pile Of Junk

There was a monster called Bip
Who used to live in a tip
His head was made from a can
He thought he was Superman
His other house was a skip
In the middle of a pit.

Simon Wallace (10)
Princetown Primary School

Gloomy Night

Tonight there is a full moon.
In the distance I saw a tomb.
As I saw a bright light
I ran with a ghostly fright.
I found a torch and switched it on.
All my fear had gone.

Willow Hufton (9)
Princetown Primary School

Gloomy Forest

There was a full moon
And behind me I heard a big boom.
I ran with all my might
I had a terrible fright.
I switched on my torch
And I ran home to my front porch.

Jennifer Graham (10)
Princetown Primary School

My Dumb Dog!

Asleep he wheezes at his ease
And unaware that he has fleas.

He hogs the fire, he bakes his head
As he lays in his comfy bed.

He's just a sack of snoring dog
Not something that you would like to snog!

When he goes to get his bone
I'm left here all on my own.

Victoria Steele (10)
Princetown Primary School

In The Dark

In the dark the small bats play
On the big rocky shore bay
On the shore, the black bats squeak
Around the corner the floorboards creak
From the distance, I hear a noise
Then I see a gang of boys
What am I really scared of?

Charmaine McDonough (10)
Princetown Primary School

IF I WON SOME MONEY

If I won some money
What would I do?
Go around the world
Or go to the zoo?
I could buy a fake skin coat
Or instead
I could buy a boat
What should I do if I won some money?
Buy a sculpture foot
Or tons of bars of chocolate?
If I won, won, won, won, won, won, won, some money
If I won, won, won, won, won, won, won, some money
Should I buy a fountain
Or climb a mountain?
Oh what should I buy if I won money?
Buy a bunny
Or a jar of honey?
What shall I buy?
What shall I buy?
Buy a pie
Or fly in the sky?
Oh I might just get a budgie!

Alexander Watson (10)
Princetown Primary School

WATERFALL

The raging rapids hurl water against the rocks,
This racing river never ever stops.
It carries it to the waterfall,
Where the thirsty bubbly springs call.
It leaps from the edge like a grasshopper,
Like from a bottle, the pull of its stopper.
It crashes loudly to the ground,
Making a loud sound.
It froths around like beer,
A lovely noise to hear.
It then expands like a forest fire,
Or even like the Roman Empire.
A waterfall is a beautiful place,
So let it fall, give it space.

Andrew Barrington (10)
St Bernard's School, Newton Abbot

THE BEACH

I walked along the beach and listened to the ocean.
My sadness was as unending as the waves.
The sea was like kisses sweet as dew.

I walked along the beach and listened to the ocean.
The sea looked as dull as ditch water.
I decided to swim and I was like a fish out of water.

I walked along the beach and listened to the ocean.
It looked as holy as dew.
I was determined to become like a duck to water.

I walked along the beach and listened to the ocean.
The waves were as a dog lapping at its drink.
I thought they sounded as a storm in the night.

Ryan Brook (9)
St Bernard's School, Newton Abbot

A PUDDLE

A puddle is like a blob of ink.
A puddle is blue not bright pink.
A puddle is cold and left by the rain.
A puddle can be a bit of a pain.

A puddle can form in a hole.
A puddle can form on the ground.
A puddle can form on the road.
A puddle is usually round.

The puddle is scared of the sun.
It's a shame that the puddle can't run.
The puddle is dried up on the floor.
The poor puddle is no more.

Kendelle Cooke (10)
St Bernard's School, Newton Abbot

WATER

Water is vibrant
Water is bold
Sometimes is hot
Sometimes is cold.

When it is hot
I use it for washing
When it is cold
I use it for sploshing

Water is fast
Water is slow
Sometimes is soft
It has a nice flow

I like it best cold
As I swim and I play
It keeps me so cool
On a hot summer's day.

Fraser Rix (10)
St Bernard's School, Newton Abbot

SNOWFLAKES

Look at the gleaming snowflakes
Dazzling in the frosty moonlight.
Six-sided stars that
twinkle in the night.
The snowflakes gently drift to the ground
floating swirling, dancing, playing
melting in the morning sunlight.

Eleanor David (8)
St Bernard's School, Newton Abbot

UNDER THE SEA

Peaceful, enchanted and gentle
Under the surface of the sea
Creatures great and small
Crawling, dashing and floating
Limpets, barnacles and shells
A wonderful display on the rocks
Under the rocks and stone
Lie fish, crabs and lobsters.
The depth of the blue sea
Looks never-ending
The golden sand at the bottom
Waiting to erupt
The light from the sun
Beams on the creatures
Making fascinating shadows
But deep, deep down
Lies another world.

Lucy Baines (10)
St Bernard's School, Newton Abbot

MY SKELETON

Look at my skeleton,
A large bag of bones.
It's as white as a sheet
The bones shiver and shake.

My skeleton clangs, clinks
And dances.

It is a cage for my heart.

Felix Attlee (8)
St Bernard's School, Newton Abbot

I Want To Paint A Poem

I want to paint a hamster
as it climbs the tube

I want to paint my mum's scream
as I put a spider down her back

I want to paint a shock of pain
when I cut myself

I want to paint the sound of marbles
as I roll them to my friends

I want to paint the fizz of Fanta
as I drink it

I want to paint the cow's moo
as I feed it grass.

Rachel Jack (9)
St Bernard's School, Newton Abbot

The River Dart

I stand by the river,
flowing as fast as a deer.
Frothing with white bubbles,
after crashing from rock to rock.

I hear the rapids gushing
and bubbling,
I thrust my hand into the greyish
blue water.
As cold as ice
Freezing!

I look down and touch the
cold and gritty sand,
The water is as clear as a
crystal.

The water as quick as lightning
shoots through the long winding
river into the glassy sea.

Edward Stuckey (10)
St Bernard's School, Newton Abbot

UNDER THE SEA

The sea is like an empty room
Echoing as you go.
The rocks are like cats' claws
Scraping and scratching.
The fish are like one big animal
Circling all together.
The reeds are like arms
Waiting to enfold you.
The coral is like a holly bush
Prickling your feet.
The waves are like gigantic storms
Crashing against the boats.
The sand is like little crumbs
Swirling around the sea.
Octopuses and like massive spiders
Clinging to their prey.

Rana El-Nashar (10)
St Bernard's School, Newton Abbot

My Garden

Rabbits jumping, leaping, hiding in the shady bushes,
Trees swaying, rustling in the wind.
Birds flying, calling from tree to tree,
That's what I like about my garden.

Mice scattering, quickly in the long grass,
Friends shouting, screaming as they play.
Dogs barking, yapping when they run,
That's what I like about my garden.

Bikes racing, whizzing down the drive,
Squirrels darting, springing, searching for nuts.
Sun shining, sparkling in the sky,
That's what I like about my garden.

Charlotte Isaacs (10)
St Bernard's School, Newton Abbot

My Dream Pet

A tiny little body, four legs that
are short
Small patches of brown on his
smooth white coat

His eyes look so sad and are very
dark brown
His ears stand up and his tail
hangs down

He's happy and friendly
a jolly good pet
The most faithful companion
a young girl could get.

Laura Jefferies (11)
St Bernard's School, Newton Abbot

WATERFALL

The waterfall in autumn
Is rushing and gushing
Crashing from rock to rock
Like a raging bull.
Swirling and spinning, making whirlpools.

Winter, frozen, like a necklace of pearls,
Glistening and sparkling,
As beautiful as a diamond,
As precious as love,
Priceless and solid.

Springtime, sunshine making it thaw,
Trickling and trickling.
Slowly melting.
Building up speed until
It's free to rush over the rocks again.

Summer, now bouncing,
Jumping, twirling, and dancing.
Rushing, as lively as a puppy,
The spray making hundreds of rainbows.

Jenny Pomeroy (10)
St Bernard's School, Newton Abbot

AS THE SNOW

As the snow
Elegantly and slowly
Flies over the giant rocky mountain,
Landing on the see-through jagged icicles
Floating over the cotton like clouds.

Annabel Pettinelli (11)
St Bernard's School, Newton Abbot

FLOWING GLASS

Flowing fast
Whirling round
Bubbling quickly
To the sound

Frogs croak
Swans float
Kingfishers diving
Salmon leaping

Deep and dark
Cold and blue
With a quiver
From a river.

James Burridge (10)
St Bernard's School, Newton Abbot

MY SKELETON

My skeleton looks like a bundle of sticks.
As smooth as skin, as white as paper.
As hard as rock and as creamy as custard.
My skeleton dances, shivers, rattles and quivers.
If I did not have a skeleton I would fall into a jelly-like heap.

Deborah Haarer (8)
St Bernard's School, Newton Abbot

WATER CHANGING

The chunky, rocky waterfall
Stood high in its place.
As big as a mountain,
The flowing water bounced off each little rock.
Shaky, clear ripples shimmering in the water
Calmly zig-zagged down the waterfall.

The little icicles held tight to the giant waterfall
As the running, murky water
Trickled down the side, from the melting icicles.
They were jagged like fangs.

The snow around the bottom
Gently melted into a slushy, muddy puddle.
It was creamy and as clear
As diamonds when the sun shone.

The ice was cracking.
Little sprinkles of water looked
Like raindrops.
It rushed along the ground
Turning and twisting.

So you see the water shyly
Went down the waterfall
Broke out of the ice and was free,
Developed into a mushy puddle
And melted from the icicles.

Water can be many different things.

Jessica Parker (9)
St Bernard's School, Newton Abbot

THE RIVER

Oozes through the ground
Whirling round and round
Dribbling through the planks
Weed is like green octopuses
Clinging to the rocks

Chattering over pebbles
Pattering down the drops
Shaping the banks
Looks like dogs scrambling
For their food

Smashing against the rocks
Piling out of the locks
Cutting through the water
Stones look like robots' heads
Facing to the ground

Meandering peacefully
Opening to the sea
It's a beautiful sight
And it's running free.

Louisa Beadel (10)
St Bernard's School, Newton Abbot

SNOWFLAKES

Look at the glistening, frozen snowflakes
Dazzling, freezing, sparkling crystals
Look at it slipping falling crunching to the ground
Sliding, reflecting, stinging your hands.
It's great to build a snowman too.

Victoria Martyn (8)
St Bernard's School, Newton Abbot

SNOWFLAKES

Look at the glistening snowflakes floating in the air,
As white as white, as frozen as frost.
Reflecting on the glowing ground.
Sliding, slipping, skidding, skating through the frozen puddles.
Colder than cold, colder than frost.
Snowing crystals dancing in the sky.

Cora Billyard (9)
St Bernard's School, Newton Abbot

SNOWFLAKES

Look at the sparkling snowflakes
Dazzling, glistening, frozen and soft.
Crunching, drifting in the air.
Reflecting, hanging, slipping sliding.
Six-sided, hexagonal stars floating
Down through the cold night sky.

Rebecca Isaacs (8)
St Bernard's School, Newton Abbot

ICICLES

Look at the frozen icicles.
Dazzling daggers, cold, frozen and hard.
Icicles hang like stalactites from frozen streams:
Hanging, dangling, thawing, dripping.
Icicles are tapering spikes of ice,
Hanging where water has dripped.

Sophie Affleck (8)
St Bernard's School, Newton Abbot

ICEBERGS

Look at the icebergs
Floating in the Arctic sea.
Gleaming, glinting,
Twinkling, dazzling
In the winter sun.

Look at the icebergs
Crashing, cracking,
Reflecting, splitting.
A huge mountain of ice
Floating in the sea.

Louise Taylor (9)
St Bernard's School, Newton Abbot

MY POEM

I can't think of a poem,
I'm not very good,
Please can you help me,
I think that you should,

Now what shall we start with,
I cannot think,
Thank you for helping
I've run out of ink.

I think that we've done it,
Let's have a look,
Yes we have done it,
Shall we put it in a book?

Natasha Harvey (11)
St Peter's CE Junior School, Tavistock

WEEKEND

Home at last
Through the door
Kick off shoes and
Dump the backpack on the floor.

Up the stairs
Quick as a hare
Turn on music and
Throw the school clothes in the air.

Phone my friend
And watch TV
Feed the hamster and
Do my homework after tea.

The weekend free
Time for fun
Enjoy the sun and
Going out and seeing everyone.

Zoë Bennett (10)
St Peter's CE Junior School, Tavistock

DIZZY DRAGON

I'm a dizzy dragon
Who delights in dancing doughnuts
Who drums on daft donkeys
Who draws on dumb dinghies
Who dreams of delightful dogs
Yes I'm a dizzy dragon!
Who doesn't know the end from the beginning
No! the beginning from *the end.*

Joseph Butcher (10)
St Peter's CE Junior School, Tavistock

The Kingfisher

I caught a glimpse of something blue,
                              green,
                              turquoise,
                              cyan,
down by the river today.

Its breast was golden, shining and glorious,
like the sun above.

It plunged and plummeted
then dived down low
into glistening water
which glinted and gleamed in the light.

I saw its brilliance disappear,
the joyous, precious sight was gone.

Sarah Stenning (10)
St Peter's CE Junior School, Tavistock

Rainbow

Red is the colour of the sunset,
Orange is the colour of a fire,
Yellow is the colour of a daffodil,
Green is the colour of the new spring leaves,
Blue is the colour of the ocean,
Indigo is the colour of the lavender field,
Violet is the colour of the mallard's wing,

This is what I think of when I see the *rainbow*.

Melissa Taylor (10)
St Peter's CE Junior School, Tavistock

FIREWORKS

The whirr of a distant
firework starts the display.

Fireworks, fireworks everywhere
The Catherine wheel is getting
dizzy as it fades away.
The golden rain splinters
into the sky.
The stars are dancing as if
they want to play.
The whiz of a rocket and then
a loud sigh.

Fireworks, fireworks everywhere.

Charlotte Bettles (10)
St Peter's CE Junior School, Tavistock

I LIKE

I like football,
I play it in the park.
Morning, noon and night,
Until it is dark.

I like rugby,
Swimming too.
I have a lot of fun
Maybe you can come too?

I like my dog Tigger,
He's really cool!
I want to play with him all the time,
But I have to go to school!

Holly Krotke (11)
St Peter's CE Junior School, Tavistock

FOUR SEASONS, FOUR FRIENDS

Autumn grabs the pretty trees
And shakes them to their death
Around the trees fall the leaves
Scattered by his breath.

Then autumn hands over to winter
Who waves his crystal white wand
An icicle hangs like a splinter,
Waiting to shatter the pond.

Then spring comes along and takes up the reins,
Spreading the blood to her flowery veins
Life jumps up and dances along
Prancing about, singing her song.

Then summer is here again,
Letting warmth out of her pen
Writing messages in the sand
Hearing the carnival's big brass band.

The music fades and the dance goes on,
Another new year marching along.

Alexandra Bathie (10)
St Peter's CE Junior School, Tavistock

DOWN ON THE RIVERBANK

Look, down on the riverbank,
Standing on the shore,
I see an otter,
Licking its paw.

Down in the depths,
A pike roams free,
I can see him,
But he can't see me.

Now I see a kingfisher,
Swooping for its prey,
Up it goes again,
oops, no trout today.

Now I spy a timid mouse,
Watching from its woodland house,
Slowly, quietly, I take a step forward,
With a flurry of movement, they're all homeward.

Charles Westwood (10)
St Peter's CE Junior School, Tavistock

THE SWEETIE JUNGLE

I crawl along the starburst path,
Licking, along the way.
I stand upon the chocolate grass,
I hope I've come to stay.

I swing through on a liquorice vine,
Attached to some jelly trees.
I hop over to taste some gum,
And see the sherbet seas!

I skid along some fizzy ice,
Then land in a juicy pool.
I run among some Smartie tigers,
This won't last five years at all.

I come to the edge of the jungle,
Where I see my bed.
'What have you been doing?' Mum asks,
'Nothing much,' I said.

Emily Atkinson (10)
St Peter's CE Junior School, Tavistock

FLOWERS

Flowers all stand in their beds,
Showing us their pretty little heads.

Look how they all strangely stand,
On the earth and on the land.

See how they grow good and fast,
Finally you see them all at last.

They make your garden look so sweet,
If you put them all so neat.

Their colours always seem to shine,
As they always look so fine.

Now the time's come for them to sleep,
Maybe tomorrow I'll hear them weep.

Carmen Luxton (11)
St Peter's CE Junior School, Tavistock

LIGHTNING

Swords of light,
Yellow and bright,
Flashes in the air.

> Jagged light,
> Blue and white,
> Thunder everywhere.

Heaven's might,
Dark and light.
Beware, beware
Beware!

Charlotte Hall (10)
St Peter's CE Junior School, Tavistock

THE FLOWER

The grass was coated
With a layer of frost,
And there in a different field,
The crocus popped its head up.

I walked to the field,
And saw a crocus sitting
It was in the ground doing nothing
You wouldn't think it was alive.

I went back a few times that day
Just to watch it grow.
It grew and grew and grew,
So tall that it nearly touched the sky.

But one day I went there,
All the petals had drooped.
It sunk back in the ground again
Ready to wait for spring.

Catherine Bryony Lake (10)
St Peter's CE Junior School, Tavistock

MY CAT IN HEAVEN

Please look after my cat
when she wanders out to play
to a cat so small and furry
I love her more each day
I wonder what she thinks of grass
and earth and sky so blue?
She knows I love her very much
and I know you love her too.

Emma Lewis (11)
St Peter's CE Junior School, Tavistock

THE MONSTERS

The monsters are under my bed
The monsters are above my head
The monsters are in the bath
The monsters are having a laugh

The monsters are under the stair
The monsters have blue hair
The monsters are in the hall
The monsters are playing ball

The monsters are under the table
The monsters are watching Cable
The monsters are at my school
The monsters are really cool

The monsters!

Sophie Clare Edwards (11)
St Peter's CE Junior School, Tavistock

THE TALKING GARDEN

Gentle breezes blow the grass
Row upon row of poppies laugh.

Daffodils chatter in the sun
Giving happiness to everyone.

This garden is a gem
Embedded in the edge of the countryside's hem.

Autumn comes with wind and rain,
The sun hides behind the clouds yet again.

Annabel Turner (10)
St Peter's CE Junior School, Tavistock

SUMMER DAYS

Bright blue skies
Blue blossom trees,
Lush green grass
Feeling the breeze.

Blinding orange sun
Birds flying high,
Red juicy tomatoes
Summer has reached the sky.

Trees lying still
Cold morning dew,
Strawberries very sweet
Everything is new.

Olivia Foster (10)
St Peter's CE Junior School, Tavistock

THE DOLPHIN

I saw something slither,
In the deep blue water.
It had a long nose,
And a shark-like fin.
I waddled up to it,
And it smiled and chuckled.
Then I swam further out towards the sea,
And the dolphin chased after me!

Emily Marks (10)
St Peter's CE Junior School, Tavistock

WHEN I AM OLDER

When I am older
I want to be a vet,
Or a doctor
I could be a nurse
Or a fireman.
I want to save people's lives,
I want to be called brave.

What about a dentist
Or a hairdresser?
I could be in the Navy,
How about a teacher?

I want to sail the seven seas
Learn to speak Japanese
No!
I want to rescue people
Show them I can do it.

No, I don't want to do any,
I don't want to grow up
I want to stay eleven
For ever and ever.

Laura Hooson (11)
St Peter's CE Junior School, Tavistock

EASTER TIME!

E   aster is a time for celebrations
A   nd of course we can't forget the eggs!
S   pringtime is here and the Easter bunny is out!
T   he trusty mums are out to hide the eggs,
                    and we're all getting excited
E   ggs are yummy but I'm glad we don't have them
                                all year round!
R   ed ones blue ones all sorts of colours, that's what
                                Easter's all about!

Hannah Willcock (10)
St Peter's CE Junior School, Tavistock

A POETRY COMPETITION

Sweating, nerves overloading,
The minutes snail by, by, by, by, by, by, by, by, by, by, by, by, by,
Thinking mouth all dry, dry, dry, dry, dry, dry, dry, dry, dry,
Dare not talk, dare not move,
Heart pounding, watch the clock,
Shivering silence,
Close my eyes, it's no use
I have to work,
In the poetry competition.

Alastair Toms (9)
Sandford Primary School

HUH?

In the field the towering grass elegantly
sways from side to side.
In the golden corn the fieldmouse
tries to hide.
In the river the otter swishes through
the muddy water.
In the farmhouse the farmer's wife
lived with the farmer's daughter.
In the zoo the animals
are wearing shoes.
In the garden the dogs
are wearing tutus.
In the park the cats are
singing a song.
In the courtroom the mayor shouts
'Something's gone extremely wrong!'

Naomi May (9)
Sandford Primary School

OUR WORLD

Let our environment grow,
Leave the wilderness be.
Let our world go round,
Let the birds sing in the trees.
Let the foxes live without hunters,
Let the bears live on their way home.
Let the wolves howl in the mountains,
Let the wind sing in the leaves.

Ellie Ruscombe-King (8)
Sandford Primary School

MY SISTERS AND ME

My sisters can be so
Aggravating.
They kick me, pinch me and
punch me.

So I give them a fight!
I kick them,
punch them,
tickle them.
But they
Howl!
Like the dog.
Mum tells me off
Sorry Yasmin!
Sorry Xanthia!

Zoë Petherick (8)
Sandford Primary School

THE CRYSTAL SEA

The crystal clear sea is the most
beautiful sea in the world.
It's been there for hundreds of years,
It's clear, full of fish, and very warm.
It's like a giant warm Jacuzzi
full of lovely fish.
I feel like a dolphin, wild in the sea
It's too beautiful to be true.
The crystal clear sea
Is just beautiful.

George Fleming (9)
Sandford Primary School

SKY HUNTER

Sky hunter of the sky,
Greater than a panther on land,
A creamy moonlit-coloured breast.
The sooty feathers, of a black coal top half.
The specks on its underside look like birds flying;
It's curved beak used as a dagger,
It's ebony, black, long tail floating behind it,
Wings soaring through,
It streams through the air,
A brush painting, wind in its face,
Like a blur in the sky.
Coming closer,
Coming closer,
But a speedy whoosh,
Quick as a flicker of flame
Fiery eyes,
Faster!
Faster!
Burning, blazing, coat shoots down from Heaven,
It strikes!
It strikes again!
Head down!
Tail raised!
Talons outstretched!
That is the power o f the peregrine falcon.

Emily Monger (8)
Sandford Primary School

HUNGRY HAMSTERS

Ten hungry hamsters sitting on a gate
Two fell off then there were eight.

Eight hungry hamsters doing magic tricks
Two disappeared then there were six.

Six hungry hamsters playing on the floor
Two got squashed then there were four.

Four hungry hamsters sneezing with the flu
Two turned green then there were two.

Two hungry hamsters eating a bun
They both went pop and then there were none.

Scott Webb (10)
Sandford Primary School

MORNING

Slug gliding up
The gravel, garden path
Disappearing into
The midst of a crack.

As a snail treads softly as it leaves
A shimmering glittered crystal trail
The sun, golden and hazy
Shines down.

Dannee McGuire (8)
Sandford Primary School

AUTUMN WIND

The autumn wind is blustery
Everything is rustling,
Leafy and blustery.
The menacing wind sweeps across the bare fields.
It howls across the world.
As the dead leaves fall and shrivel
up into medium balls,
The rustly wind
creaks in every house
And taps on the windows
I lie up in bed,
It's like the wind is calling me
But as I wake it's gone.

Matthew Brassington (8)
Sandford Primary School

A SNOWY OWL BABY

A snowy owl baby,
as round as a snowball,
as creamy as milk,
a ball of feathers,
as soft as silk,
as its sharp beady eyes,
glint in the sun,
victims run.

Zoë Grenyer Matthews (9)
Sandford Primary School

EVIL WIND

The winter wind is icy and cold,
It's so evil and menacing,
Swishing and harsh,
It blows rock hard in your face,
It howls through open doors,
When it blows you,
You feel like frozen ice,
It whistles through the bare branches of trees.
The winter wind is icy and cold,
It's so evil and menacing,
When it rattles the branches of the bare trees,
It whispers a secret never to be told.

Jamie Barnes (10)
Sandford Primary School

THE EAGLE

Golden wings remind me of heaven,
Eyes as bright as a flame,
Beaks as sharp as an axe,
How I wish it was tame
It's as beautiful as the sun rising on the horizon,
Soaring high in the sky,
So stunning,
How I wish I could fly.

Megan King (8)
Sandford Primary School

MY NIGHTMARE BIRTHDAY

At my birthday we had:
Toffee tinged coffee,
Mustard flavoured custard,
Fudged sludge,
Ginger gloop,
Each a Marmite ice-cream scoop.

If you drank the lemonade
You would call the fire brigade.
As well as a game of eat blue glue,
I'm sure you'd faint at the state of the loo.

For drinks, oh dear,
Ten tons of beer,
All of them I must say tasted rather queer.

But there is one thing without a doubt,
That I admit I have left out . . .
Everyone was sick at least ten times.
Mum still hasn't got suspicious,
But I don't think that she will.
But when I think about it now I still feel very ill!

Maya Grantham (8)
Sandford Primary School

MY LOVELY DOG, HESS

My lovely dog, Hess,
She plays with me when I am happy,
She nuzzles me when I am sad and lonely,
When she sniffs it sounds like a helicopter,
She makes me feel like I am the luckiest boy on Earth,
She makes my family feel like it's bigger than it is.

James Trigg (9)
Sandford Primary School

My Best Friend, Ben

My best friend, Ben
is very special to me.
I met him in Exeter Hospital
when I was seven days old.
From then on we have been special.
We always like the same things,
he has something magic in him.
Ben's always there for me.

Jack Salisbury (9)
Sandford Primary School

My Sweet Cats

My sweet cats, they eat all day.
They're as black as the night, like a streak of black lightning.
Their claws are as sharp as the ends of daggers.
They remind me of happiness.
When I'm lonely they make me comfy
When I'm happy they purr.

Laurence Honeysett (9)
Sandford Primary School

My Dog

My dog is called Chloe and she is just great,
she loves chocolate, biscuits, bones and cake.
She makes my mum cross when she climbs on my bed,
especially when she's covered in mud that is red.
She never gets cross even when my sister hurts her,
I love her lots and she is my best friend.

Jemima Bowyer (8)
Sandford Primary School

THE WINTER WIND

The winter wind is such a thing,
bitterly cold
an icy sting.
I hate it
especially at night,
when I have to turn off the light.
I hear the rattling from the old creaky barn,
I feel the draught from the crannies
in the window,
and see twinkling from the stars.
Finally at the dead of night
I lose my sight,
and drift off to dreamland.

Louie Sandys (8)
Sandford Primary School

THE WIND

When the days are the coldest
and the nights are the longest.
The children are all in bed.
The wind is calm
and the moon is sparkling
and the velvet sky glistens.
The seas smash on the rocks.
The warm wind feels hot like the sun.
The faint howl of the wind.

Emma Cartlidge (9)
Sandford Primary School

A Stormy Day

The winter wind is howling like a fox in the trees
It tries to blow me off my feet.
The winter wind goes up through your hat
and smashes in your face.
My feet are freezing when I go to bed.
The wind is rattling my windows and I can't get to sleep.
People having fun outside in the winter wind and shouting
Blow!
I wish I was out there.
The wind is chilly like an icy drink.
The wind is just like a motor bike.
The wind is a devil.
The wind is over at last.

Shaun James Hawkins (10)
Sandford Primary School

Winter

The winter wind is strong and menacing
blowing trees about.
Rabbits in their burrows
hiding from the strong wind.
Birds comforting their babies,
leaves blowing off the treetops.
Houses nearly blowing away.
The wind is harsh
people inside where it's nice
and warm.

Lee Voisey (8)
Sandford Primary School

ON THE WAY

I am a moving person,
I stay with my mum most of the time.
I go to my dad's every second weekend,
and I feel very weird inside.
When my little sister cries
when she doesn't want to go,
I feel anger whirling inside from my stomach,
up to my throat where it hurts the most.
But when we get there I feel fine,
and I settle in for a while and can have a happy time.
When I come back I already miss
the other side very much.

Yah-Wan McClelland (9)
Sandford Primary School

MY PLAYFUL KITTEN

My playful kitten
He rolls around the floor
Rough, cuddly, soft
As sweet as candyfloss
As soft as a cloud
I love him
I feel as happy as a clown when I am around him
My playful kitten
He makes me feel very happy.

Rachel Cann (10)
Sandford Primary School

MY SECRET GARDEN

In my secret garden,
There's a silver polar bear,
A blazing stripy tiger
And a dull grey elephant.

In my secret garden,
There's a forest full of tall shadowy trees,
Long grass that goes up to my knees.

In my secret garden,
There is a secret door,
Beyond the secret door,
Is my home.

The secret garden was my home.
I wish my secret garden was true.

Roxanne North (9)
Sandford Primary School

THE WINTER WIND

The wild winter wind,
So icy, so evil,
Howling so harsh, making people shiver,
The icy winter wind,
So killing, so devious,
Whistling, so cruel,
Whistling, so mean,
Being so grim, but exciting.

Noah Mosley (9)
Sandford Primary School

THE STORM

The storm comes clashing down to Earth
Making children cry, parents worry
Dogs, howl, cats scurry
The storm comes clashing down to Earth
Giving destruction another birth.

The storm comes clashing down to Earth
Breaking windows, smashing tiles
Blowing down trees, flooding isles
The storm comes clashing down to Earth

The storm comes clashing down to Earth
One million thoughts run through your head
Whilst you're drowsy in your bed
The storm comes clashing down to Earth
Giving destruction another birth.

Joshua Coyle (9)
Sherwell Valley County Primary School

MY CAT

My cat is fluffy, like a snowball,
As good as can be,
So brown as the tree trunk of an apple tree,
Eyes like the green, bright grass,
A nose, as wet as the sea,

My cat likes to play, to jump and run,
She loves her treats, her favourite food,
But she is my favourite *cat*

Jodie Matthews (8)
Sherwell Valley County Primary School

ELEPHANT

A big nose
A tiny pose.

A tiny tail
A flat nail.

A hard bang
A huge gang.

A long trunk
A hard clunk.

A hard stomp
A vibrating chomp.

       A catalogue to make me
             Elephant!

Shabnam Roughani (10)
Sherwell Valley County Primary School

MY CAT

My cat is snowy as the snow and snowdrops.
My cat is silver with golden hair that shines like the sun.
My cat is dark, dark, dark as the deepest sea.
My cat is the top of the shiny stars
And bright as tinsel.
My cat is beautiful and clever as any computer.

I love and adore my cat.

Laura Dalton (7)
Sherwell Valley County Primary School

BUTTERFLIES

I saw a butterfly in the sky
flittering and flapping with such
colourful wings which shine.
I love butterflies.
I like how they fly so high
up in the sky.

So soft are their wings.
As light as a feather floating
in the sky.
How I love watching them float
as they fly into the sky, up, up and away.

Hayley Byrne (10)
Sherwell Valley County Primary School

THE YEAR

As jolly as January.
As fierce as February.
As merry as March.
As happy as April.
As sunny as May.
As jumpy as June.
As bouncy as July.
As breezy as August.
As soggy as September.
As leafy as October.
As naughty as November.
As dark as December.

Kriss Hudson (8)
Sherwell Valley County Primary School

Cow

My cow has a nose that is wet, like an ice cube.
Her coat is silky, like hair.
She is black, like a rug.
She is white, like the snow.
Her horns curve like a new moon.
She is heavy, like a box.
Her hooves are black, like the night.

Harriet Payne (8)
Sherwell Valley County Primary School

Down In The Cellar

Milk bottles stored for next year
A cat that's been trapped for years
A picture of an ancient mummy
A knife that's been rusting for years
A mouse that's been half-eaten
A tramp with no clothes.

Graham North (9)
Sherwell Valley County Primary School

Space

Space is as black as a witch's heart.
Space is never-ending.
You could explore it forever and ever.
Space is very dangerous because
it hasn't any gravity applied,
so you could float away.
Space is brilliant.

Andrew Crask (10)
Sherwell Valley County Primary School

COLOUR ALPHABET

A ctive yellow growls after you,
B rown comes to stare at you,
C reamy blue smiles at you,
D irty grey spits at you,
E normous peach throws fruit at you,
F ishy orange blows orange juice at you,
G reen is kind to you,
H orrible red makes faces at you,
I gnorant white waves at you,
J umping purple jumps to you,
K icking black kicks you,
L ime licks you,
M opping mauve mops its way to you,
N ice violet plays violins to you,
O ccupied gold throws gold money at you,
P opular turquoise just turns away from you,
Q uiet silver just hits you and walks away from you,
R ich bronze robs all your stuff,
S illy luminous blue shines its way to you,
T he silvery pink is asleep 'Shhh'
U just will never know this colour,
V icious navy spits gravy at you,
W icked multicolour makes scary faces at you,
X is secret so don't ask me,
Y ucky khaki thinks he's lush,
Z -zz this colour's asleep.

Kirstyn Carpenter (8)
Sherwell Valley County Primary School

IT MIGHT BE

My brother found a present,
he put it to his ear,
'I wonder what it is?'
'I dare you to open it.' said my sister.
It might be a dancer with trainers on,
or a Cheshire cat's smile.
Or it might be a baby's face,
or chickenpox from a hen.
Or it could be a peacock that's black and white,
It might be a snowman with a football kit on.
Or it could be a tiger that quacks like a duck,
or it could be a lion that likes to sing nursery rhymes.
Or it might be a blonde-haired girl that's got hairy legs.
(He opens it quickly)
'What, a book?'

Chelsea Payne (9)
Sherwell Valley County Primary School

THE BATTLE

Bang! Bang! Go the guns.
Boom! Go the bombs,
blood spilt everywhere,
bullets firing everywhere.
Charge! Go the men into combat,
fighting for their place in history.
Here come the cavalry charging into the door of death,
meeting their fate on the horses while wives are sad
and brave for those who need help with the wounded and dead.

Thomas Linskey (10)
Sherwell Valley County Primary School

STORMS

The rain lashes down, down,
Making water brown, brown.
People are getting wet, wet,
But don't you fret, fret.
There are shelters near, near,
Come on in here, here,
It is very warm, warm,
But not out in the storm, storm,
Here, grab a towel, towel,
My, how you howl, howl.
I don't think you like rain, rain,
You are such a pain, pain.
Yes, I know you're a dog, dog
And not a hog, hog.
Lie by the fire, fire,
I know it's your desire, desire,
Where you can dry, dry,
As time flies by, by.

Jade Hudson (10)
Sherwell Valley County Primary School

COLOUR POEM

Blue is the colour of the sky
Brown is the colour of a horse
Purple is the colour of a parrot
Green is the colour of the grass
White is the colour of an Arctic fox
Black is the colour of a cow
Yellow is the colour of the sun
Grey is the colour of a rainy day

Lewis Hodgson (8)
Sherwell Valley County Primary School

HAPPINESS

Happiness is a flow of all the colours of the world.
Happiness is a smell like fresh berries out of the garden.
Happiness tastes like strawberries out of a strawberry field.
Happiness is a noise that sounds like leaves rustling in the wind.
Happiness feels like a cloud up in the sky.
Happiness lives up in Heaven.

Jenna Dalton (9)
Sherwell Valley County Primary School

THE SILLY KITTEN

My silly kittens, as playful as can be
She's always running away, chasing her
Little tail as fast as she can,
She's always as playful as can be.
I love my silly kitten very much.
She's as black as night, as brown
As dead leaves and as white as snow.

Liam Botham (8)
Sherwell Valley County Primary School

HAPPINESS

Happiness is as red as a lip
It smells of fruit in the garden
It tastes of strawberries
Happiness sounds like the wind blowing
It feels like liquid
It lives in people's hearts.

Jessica Brown (10)
Sherwell Valley County Primary School

THE BAT

It was in the middle of the night,
A bat went past on his flight.
There were sounds of the whistling wind,
Which felt like a cold little pond.
It had smells like a sunflower in the summer,
And it looked like a silver stream flowing through the sky.
There was one passing by the silver moonlight,
It was only in its childhood, about five or six
And it moved like a rocket, past planets.

Melissa Jayne Skirrow (9)
Sherwell Valley County Primary School

SORROW

Sorrow is as purple as a wizard's heart,
Sorrow lives in a dragon's cave.
Sorrow smells as bad as the smoke from a fire,
Sorrow tastes like an apple squashed by an elephant,
It sounds as bad as the waves crashing against the rocks
on a stormy winter's night.
Sorrow feels as hard as a rock.

Claire Bovey (10)
Sherwell Valley County Primary School

DEATH

The colour of death is a black sky,
The smell of death is unemptied bins.
The taste of death is sour.
The sound of death is eerie.

Marc Carrer (10)
Sherwell Valley County Primary School

THE MONSTER

The monster is called Buffstation,
He lives in the Devil's cave,
It has the horns of a bull,
He has the snake's staring eyes,
His body is a wolf's body but with eagle's wings.
He only comes out at night,
Everyone makes sure he can't get near them,
It is a bloodthirsty beast with no care for other things,
His idea of a juicy roast dinner is people,
A goat is like a teeny crisp,
Considering it's about their size.
It is exceedingly treacherous,
It could beat a minotaur in a fight,
So if you ever see one all you have to do is *run!*

Sam Darke (9)
Sherwell Valley County Primary School

INSIDE THE FOX

Inside the fox's paw, a streaming river flows.
Inside the streaming river, the fox's claw.
Inside the fox's claw, some windy sand dunes.
Inside the windy sand dunes, the fox's fur.
Inside the fox's fur, a big city.
Inside the big city, the fox's blood.
Inside the fox's blood, a rainbow of colour.
Inside the rainbow of colour, the fox's eye.
Inside the fox's eye, a sewing needle
which is dug in to the fox's paw.

Dominic James Bowles (9)
Sherwell Valley County Primary School

THE GIRAFFE FROM BOTSWANA

Giraffe is ancient, huge and old
But not yet has been sold
Someone has bartered to buy
But the time doesn't fly by.

Giraffe has suffered bumps and bruises
But not once has Giraffe been on cruises
But an English chap
Who was discovering African sap
When he needed some assistance
He was travelling into the distance.

Giraffe had said before
'I think Gazza might score.'
The English chap laughed
And looked at Giraffe
He said 'You are funny,
But not half as cute as a bunny.

Shouldn't you be sleeping peacefully in your bed?'
The giraffe answered 'Use your head.'
The clatter and bang
As the English man sang
'Giraffe, Giraffe
You're taller than a calf
And you don't half make me laugh!'

Calum Jones (9)
Sherwell Valley County Primary School

RAIN AND SUN

When it starts to rain, babies start to cry.
Small children go mad and cry when the rain gets their hair wet.
Rain falls, splitter, splatter, splatter, splitter.
it taps on our window as if someone was knocking on the window,
You go to school in the rain, drip, drip, drip, you get wet through.
Finally get to school drenched, cold, hair wet.
In class you look out of the window.
The rain is stopping, it's only spitting, spitting, spitting.
Mrs Murphy says 'Get to work!'
I look out the window and what do I see?
Yes, that's right, the hot sun
As red as Africa's hottest day in summer.

Samantha Nunn (10)
Sherwell Valley County Primary School

THE MAGIC ROSE

As the rose goes through the door,
it opens a very big latch,
Click, click
It starts to get smaller and smaller
inside the door it meets people and
it gets smaller, it reaches the garden.
In the garden is a water feature and flowers
as far as the eye can see.
There's a dog to play with,
and a ball, Splash! Splash! In the pond
The rose went to a different place.

Stephanie Matthews (10)
Sherwell Valley County Primary School

THE ROARING TIGER

Roaring tiger,
Big, sharp teeth,
A swingy tail
Running legs
And a big roar.

Shiny teeth,
A mouth eating meat,
Glowing eyes
And pointy ears.

Softest fur,
Stripes like
Summer, winter
And all the months.

Jack Mooney (8)
Sherwell Valley County Primary School

PEACE

Peace smells like a turkey cooking,
Peace is as yellow as the sun,
Peace tastes like a cooked turkey,
Peace sounds like a boy shouting 'Yes,'
Peace feels like picking up a rose,
Peace lives in an old man's heart,
Peace is a kind grandad, giving you a sweet,
Peace is as caring as Mum's heart.

Lloyd Falconer (10)
Sherwell Valley County Primary School

UNDER THE OCEAN

Tropical fish, swimming
around in part of the sea,
their colours are a splash
of a rainbow.

In another part of the sea
lives an oyster with a pearl
tucked under his shell.

In another part of the sea
lives a dolphin splashing
and spluttering in the ocean
with its friends.

In another part of the sea
lives an octopus letting out
all the ooze as it swims along.

In another part of the sea
lives a whale squirting and
spraying water from the
little hole on the top of his
smooth back.

Lucy Cook (10)
Sherwell Valley County Primary School

MY BEAR

My bear has white ears, like the stars in the sky.
My bear has lovely yellow eyes, bright like the sun.
My bear has orange paws, like oranges.
My bear has a lovely, black, furry coat.
My bear is lovely.

Jasmine Mangan (8)
Sherwell Valley County Primary School

THE YEAR

As icy as January
As stormy as February
As windy as March
As new as April
As sunny as May
As light as June
As tiring as July
As beachy as August
As good as September
As dark as October
As scary as November
As cold as December.

Sean Adderley (7)
Sherwell Valley County Primary School

THE YEAR

As jolly as January
As fishy as February
As merry as March
As annoying as April
As menacing as May
As jumpy as June
As gentle as July
As ordinary as August
As silent as September
As honest as October
As naughty as November
As dark as December.

Nicholas Bush (8)
Sherwell Valley County Primary School

Kenning Lightning

I can tear your house to shreds,
When you're all in your beds.

I can frighten your little children,
I can give you a great shock.

I can make the sea or rivers blow.

I am worse than thunder,
I am terribly frightening.

If you are paddling you won't be for long,
I will send your boat spinning along.

Ashley Grimes (10)
Sherwell Valley County Primary School

Dolphin

My dolphin has a curly tail
with a fin,
he has fun.
He jumps and dives
all over the ocean.
He has two eyes.

My dolphin is as beautiful as
ten roses in a row.
He is as clever as
a sparkling computer.

Jordan Edgecombe (8)
Sherwell Valley County Primary School

MIDNIGHT LIGHT

Midnight light
How bright
Fly like a kite
Always so bright.

Egg moon, diamond star
That's the light
How bright
Kitten likes the light
Stars shining on the bar.

I like the star
On the bar
Bright egg moon
Bright diamond star
Twinkle in the sky.

Lauren Amy Kilner (8)
Sherwell Valley County Primary School

THE SLITHERY SNAKE

Snakes slither on the ground,
Their skins sparkle in the sun
They open their mouths very wide
They have fangs that are very sharp
They are totally dangerous,
Snakes have scales on their backs
They raise their heads high above the ground.

Skene Matthews (8)
Sherwell Valley County Primary School

THE YEAR

As beautiful as January,
As stoney as February,
As lovely as March,
As windy as April,
As jolly as May,
As sunny as June,
As good as July,
As dark as August,
As smiley as September,
As great as October,
As windy as November,
As Christmassy as December.

Jade Smith (7)
Sherwell Valley County Primary School

A MONTH POEM

As snowy as January,
As stormy as February,
As new as March,
As fresh as April,
As pretty as May,
As jolly as June,
As sunny as July,
As kind as August,
As careful as September,
As happy as October,
As dark as November,
As joyful as December.

Georgia Walters (8)
Sherwell Valley County Primary School

FOOTBALL TEAM ALPHABET

A rsenal play like they don't care.

B radford spit on the pitch as they play.

C helsea think they're top of the league.

D ublin watch football all day long.

E ngland love their manager so much they faint.

F ootball teams are great and strong.

G loucestershire don't care about things they do.

H eaven's sake! Blackpool are rubbish!

I   ... (this team's a secret so don't tell anyone!)

J umping across the pitch comes the referee with his cards.

K eepers are rubbish didn't you know?

L inesmen stare at you when you kick the ball offside.

M anchester United yes! They're the best!

N ewcastle United wear black and white.

O ld Trafford's the name for a ground you know.

P ests are most footballers crawling along the ground.

Q ueen's Park Rangers think they're the best in the world.

R overs are rubbish. I just found out.

S underland fiddle around on the pitch.

T orquay United, well they're sort of the best.

U toxeter are the bottom of the league.

V enomous players jump around on the pitch.

W allingford USA, they're the best (only kidding).

X ... (this team hasn't been invented yet)

Y es! Yet again another goal!

Z ipping the ball through the goal!

Gareth Jones (7)
Sherwell Valley County Primary School

ANIMAL ALPHABET

A   n ant look at you.
B   ears roar at you.
C   himpanzees and their babies laugh at you.
D   eers are so sad they glare and stare at you.
E   agles don't like people and stare at you.
F   lamingoes just stand and stare at you.
G   iraffes, with their long necks look at you.
H   yenas laugh and make funny faces at you.
I   guanas, like snakes, hiss at you.
J   ellyfish like to zap you.
K   angaroos like jumping at you and want to bounce with you.
L   eopards are so proud they just ignore you and don't like you.
M   ice like waking and seeing and looking at you.
N   ightingales like staying out at night and singing to you.
O   wls to see you in the dark and say 'Tu whoo!'
P   enguins flap at you.
Q   uack! Quack! silly ducks quack at you.
R   hinoceros hug and puff at you.
S   eagulls look down at you.
T   igers roll and roar towards you.
U   nicorns puzzle you (because you thought they didn't exist)
V   ultures look at you,
W   alrus' look at you.
X   . . . (this creature's name is a secret)
Y   ou can see these animals in this strange zoo!
Z   oo-keepers keep their eye on you too!

Holly McLauchlan (8)
Sherwell Valley County Primary School

A Continuation Of The Pied Piper

The Pied Piper did his worst,
He played his pipe till he burst,
The children came in his curse.
As soon as the mayor heard, this he did not like,
He scratched his head and fed his pike,
The people came but oh! This was a fright.
The piper led the children through the night,
He took them to a place, through a cave.

The mayor cried, 'Why didn't I behave?'
The piper played for a day,
The children had to live on hay.
The mayor said, 'Oh why didn't I pay?'
The piper came,
He paid his debts,
And the children came with their pets.
A party was made,
No need for the aid.
So there was once a Pied Piper of Hamelin.

David Grove (11)
Sherwell Valley County Primary School

My Cat

My cat is like the sun setting
And is good as can be.
My cat has blue eyes like the blue sky.
My cat is so beautiful
When she turns around she purrs at you.
My cat can do loads of tricks.

Sarah White (8)
Sherwell Valley County Primary School

THE COMPETITION

There's a poem competition,
For children in year six,
To help me write a good one,
I'll need my Weetabix.

It will have to be catchy,
And interesting too,
Just hold on a second -
I need to go the loo.

Ahh, that's better,
My thinking cap's on.
My brain will have to work hard,
Before the time is gone.

Wait, I've got an idea,
Though it's took me rather long.
I'll have to write it down quick,
Before I hear the . . . *Gong!*

Jessica Coyle (10)
Sherwell Valley County Primary School

DECEMBER DRAUGHT

Whistling
A misty voice
Like the moaning of a child
The draught blows through the air cold and
Blowing . . .

Kerri Tucker (10)
Sherwell Valley County Primary School

KNICKERLESS!

I was only a little girl,
when I was in class 1,
I used to always do a twirl,
when I danced on.

Anyway, this is a different story,
it is extremely embarassing,
I had to get ready for PE
and found something was missing.

I boiled red as people laughed,
everyone was getting changed,
behind the table I crouched,
as a line was being formed.

When the line was leading down,
I gathered all my courage,
went to see Mrs Dawn,
and told her of my worries.

Finally the room was empty
and the lights were turned out,
I went and found my clothes quickly
and gave a big shout . . .

I can't do PE!

Julier Bailey (10)
Sherwell Valley County Primary School

SNOWFLAKE

I'd like to be a snowflake,
Float high up in the sky,
I'd live for ever and ever,
I'd never ever die.

I'd like to be a snowflake,
A whitish one perhaps,
And fly all day and blow around
With other snowflake chaps.

I'd never have to do these things,
No homework, jobs or chores,
Just carried by the gentle wind,
With snowflakes and their snores!

I wouldn't have to sit exams,
No need to tidy rooms,
No need to even feed the cat,
Or wash the dirty spoons.

Not a thing for me to do,
I'll put the story in its place,
If you're wondering how my story ends,
I vanished without a trace!

Kim Leonard (10)
Sherwell Valley County Primary School

JANUARY CAT HAIKU

January cat
Makes paw prints across the snow
Just like a big bear.

Anthoney Richmond (10)
Sherwell Valley County Primary School

COLD AIR

After autumn it is winter's go.
I can float and drift, but I'll never know
Which house is warm, so I'll make it cold,
I will tell you a secret that has never been told.
I can't get through walls, or blankets of wool,
But I can make a cow's breath steam, as well as a bull.
I can freeze your feet and bite at your toes,
I can numb your fingers and nip your nose.

Laura Adams (10)
Sherwell Valley County Primary School

KENNING

A small, little flea-infested furball,
A cuddly thing with a tail,
The little powder puff loves to scratch,
They have nine beautiful lives,
They are great climbers,
A catalogue to make a cat!

Naomi Mooney (10)
Sherwell Valley County Primary School

WEMBLEY

Twin towers;
What a cool match,
Never a penalty,
Colchester beat Torquay,
Helped by the spot.

Luke Adderley (10)
Sherwell Valley County Primary School

SOMETHING IN THE BATH

Millions upon millions in my bath,
Pop, pop, pop in my bath,
Smelling sweetly of strawberries, pineapple smell,
Round and soft pop, pop, moving gently across the bath.
One, two, three, lots and lots of them,
I bet you know what I am talking about?
Just in case you don't, here is a clue,
Pop, pop in the bath, splash . . . so soon they all go,
But they are fun while they last,
You have guessed it!
Here are all the clues: Pop, pop they go,
Millions upon millions in my bath,
Smells go up my nose.
I don't need to give you any more clues,
You have guessed it,
Bubbles!

Abbie Clements (10)
Sherwell Valley County Primary School

OOEY GOOEY

Ooey Gooey was a worm,
A brave worm was he.
He sat upon the railroad,
A train he did not see.
Chuff, chuff, splutter, splutter,
Ooey Gooey - peanut butter.
He said goodbye and then he was dead,
With one great train wheel on his head!

Christian Frost (11)
Sherwell Valley County Primary School

CLASS POEM 6R

Luke Adderley got hurt badly
Reece Asplen takes an aspirin
Juliet Bailey is best friends with Kayleigh
Rebecca Bolton likes The Waltons
Ben Brett never forgets
Jake Brewer looks like a skewer
Sophie Clift plays in the lift
Ben Cowell is as wise as an owl
Jessica Coyle thinks she is royal
Kayleigh Drake likes eating cake
Alex Faulkner likes to walk there
Christian Frost went and got lost
Ashley Grimes is good at rhymes
Carley Hall is very small
Chris Harding is a darling
David Helliwell likes Geri Halliwell
Jamie Higham will never buy them
Jessica Lack will take the flack
Kim Leonard uses her pen hard
Jessica Lesley likes Elvis Presley
Matthew Lewis likes to chew bits
Rebecca Meaden is always readin'
Naomi Mooney is a loony
Wayne Morgan plays the organ
Emma Pearce is most fierce
Christian Radford comes from Bradford
Kim Rasmussen should learn to loosen
Anthony Richmond has learned to itch them
Lucy Runham will always stun 'em
Gracie Skirrow runs like an arrow
Carl Tucker is even luckier
Lucinda Williamson is one in a billion
Laura Wood is very good.

Ben Thomas Cowell (10)
Sherwell Valley County Primary School

A Kenning Creator

A round cave
A swirly wave,

A lump of green
A skinny bean.

A hanging worm
A squiggly squirm,

A drooping flower
A bit of power,

A hanging silk
A buttery milk,

A catalogue to make
        Me a butterfly!

Amy Madge (10)
Sherwell Valley County Primary School

Beasts

Their claws are spiky,
Their skin is greenish with mould,
They come to get you.

Andrew Broadhurst (11)
Sherwell Valley County Primary School

The Rising Sun

The sun is rising.
The bluish and pinkish sky,
Like a multicoloured ball.

Aaron Aris
Sherwell Valley County Primary School

A Pied Piper Continuation

In a rage the Piper flew
When in the street his pipe he blew,
Four strange notes the pipe it sounded
Behind the Piper children bounded,
Hypnotised by appealing music,
Up the hill without a grumbling,
Children bouncing, racing, tumbling,
Then to their ears a mighty rumbling
As on the hill a great door
Opened with a mighty roar,
All skipped into inky black
And not one looked aback,
Only one remained outside
A crippled boy with an aching side.
He hopped back to Hamelin town
And not once did he topple down.
He told the townsfolk of the happening,
Beginning with the gentle rapping.

Barnaby Davies & Matthew Rowe (11)
Sherwell Valley County Primary School

Summer Sounds

Glistening
Birds chattering
Like giggling schoolgirls.
Sounds of the waves
O'er the pebbles,
Warming.

Emma Moore (10)
Sherwell Valley County Primary School

CARS

As smooth as a baby's bottom,
Squeaking tyres make the atmosphere,
When driving, not a tear.
Bodywork amazes ready for
High speed chases.

A roar like a lion,
An amazing sense handling,
Can drive you into financial difficulty,
Prices ranging high and low,
Showrooms nationwide,
Simply . . . buy!

Weekly payment will be fine
As long as you can pay on time.

Joseph Kirollos (10)
Sherwell Valley County Primary School

FIRE

I flicker my flames and burn people's fleshy skin,
I can light up a room, as dim as dim.
I'm sad, no one likes me, whatever I do,
I just can't help myself, I don't want to hurt you.
Little sparks come outwards from my flaming fire,
But when I am angry, I become very dire.
Please don't enrage me, I won't start a riot,
If you leave me alone, I'll lie quiet as quiet.

Joe Chudley (10)
Sherwell Valley County Primary School

GINNY

My dog Ginny is a lovely lass,
She is a dog of the highest class.
She digs up stones
And she chews up bones
My marvellous dog Ginny.

Ginny has a friend called Rosie
Who sniffs her with her big, wet nosie.
They could play all day,
But sometimes Rosie stays away,
My Ginny's friend Rosie.

My dog Ginny doesn't howl at the moon.
She isn't a werewolf sort of goon.
She'll lick you all night
And give you a play fight,
My superb dog Ginny!

Sam Dodge (11)
Sherwell Valley County Primary School

ANGELS

A nyone can hear the angels sing
N earer and nearer you can hear a loud ring
G uarding everyone from danger
E agerly sitting by the manger
L ove is all around the Earth
S inging aloud because of Christ's birth

Laura McDonald (10)
Sherwell Valley County Primary School

MR DONUT

Filled with chocolate and yummy.
It's lovely in my tummy.
Can be filled with jam and cream,
Never too extreme.
I like it with jam,
It's quite nice with ham.
Some say put it in the bin.
Others say it's a sin.
Some lick it around the side
And open mouths wide.
The donut is chewy,
It's not at all gooey.
I can eat twenty-four
And still want more.
Just one more lick,
Oh, I feel quite sick!

Karl Youlden (11)
Sherwell Valley County Primary School

CANDLES

White, smooth, wavy skin,
Drips roll down my thin body,
Like rain pouring down.

Leah Winstone (11)
Sherwell Valley County Primary School

MOVING ON

It seems so far away,
like forever and a day,
just like it did
when I was a kid.
When I came to this school,
it was so big and I was so small.
Now I'm eleven, going into year seven,
it won't be the same, it will be a totally different game.
No more simple math,
I'll be taking a whole different path.
It won't be easy, it may not be fun,
but at the end of the day it has to be done.
When this day comes I'm sure I'll be fine,
'cause I'll be learning how to earn a dime.
I'll be doing new things that will help me in life,
they may even help me get a good wife,
but besides all the laughter,
besides all the fun,
there is one thing that has to be done.
The things that I'll dread,
the things I won't like,
but I'll have to revise
and give them a try.
They begin in 'E' and end in 'S',
I think that you can guess the rest!

Mario Panayiotou (11)
Sherwell Valley County Primary School

TYPES OF DOGS

Spaniels, Labradors, Greyhounds and more,
All have cute noses
And sniff around pink posies,
That's what they're so good for!

Labradors have sleek, slender breasts,
While some of the Spaniel breed
Are just there to have a feed,
But they're just as cute as the rest!

The noses and tails of dogs
Sniff and don't stop wagging
With other types of breed they are sagging
All the while when jumping through the logs.

Bryony Jones (11)
Sherwell Valley County Primary School

CHRISTMASTIME

The white, fluffy snow
Falls down from the silky sky,
Like a soft pillow.

Michelle North (11)
Sherwell Valley County Primary School

CHRISTMAS HAIKU

I hang on a tree,
I shine like the sun on Monday,
I can be multicoloured.

Alex Smith (11)
Sherwell Valley County Primary School

WHITE EGG

A white egg
A tiny keg

A slithering worm
A squiggling squirm

A hairy top
A hanging mop

A wing's sprung
A song's sung

A flying duty
A singing beauty

A catalogue to make me
A butterfly.

Kelly Tarpey (11)
Sherwell Valley County Primary School

SPARKLING TIDE

Sparkling sea shines,
Seagulls whining whines.

Wild whales jumping,
rocky, rocks bumping.

Bubbles bubbling high,
sun shines by.

Day draws by,
whales wave goodbye!

Meghan McCrory (10) & Nathalie Parsons
Tedburn St Mary Primary School

THE DARK WOODS

The dark woods,
A cool wind whips
With the beating breeze
And the whistling trees.

The dark woods,
Rolling water gently drips
As they softly fizzle free
Around me.

The dark woods,
All around the owl hoots,
Echoing through and through,
Then the silent, evil breath gently
Follows too.

The dark woods,
As I walk by,
The woods seem to lie
And pull me closer, why?

The dark woods
As the light comes closer,
The ghost goes,
Midnight close.

Megan Dennis (10)
Tedburn St Mary Primary School

SPARKLING SEA

Big whales wading,
White waves fading,
Misty sea spraying,
Tripping tide fraying.

Dolphins dip merrily,
Sharks search hungrily,
Silently spume glides,
Crazy crab hides.

Daring diver swims,
Shark hunts him,
Ship starts sinking,
People start shrieking.

Christopher Parnell (10) & Kayleigh Lucas (9)
Tedburn St Mary Primary School

SEA SPRAY

Speeding, sparkling tides,
Dolphins giving rides,
Shining shells in the sun,
Gleaming like currant buns.

Mist moves away
To bring another day,
Sunset on the shore,
Seaweed brings galore.

Ships sit upon the waves,
Not crashing into caves,
Screaming seagulls chatter,
Lapping waves they clatter.

Sophie Collins (10)
Tedburn St Mary Primary School

HAUNTED!

Twinkling stars,
Shimmering moon,
Black sky,
Almost night noon.

Dark forest,
Wind cools,
Ghostly trees,
Night rules.

Twinkling stars,
Shimmering moon,
Black sky,
Almost night noon.

Ghastly ghouls,
Petrifying phantoms,
Shadowy spectres,
Haunted wood.

Twinkling stars,
Shimmering moon,
Black sky,
Almost night noon.

Lindsey Pike (10)
Tedburn St Mary Primary School

SEA SONG

Sea ships sinking,
Screeching seagull winking.

Sea spray splashes,
Toppling tide crashes.

Salty ships sailing,
Sloshing sea waiting.

Wind's movement mild,
Whales wandering wild.

Seamen singing loud,
Wind catching clouds.

Stars shining bright,
Through the night.

James Allen (9)
Tedburn St Mary Primary School

SEA POEM

Misty mysterious waves
Bashing, crashing, caves,
Spume spraying sails,
Wishing wet whales.

See seagulls screaming,
Coral's glamour gleaming,
Baby birds whining,
Whooshing waves climbing,
Diving, dancing dolphins.

Elizabeth Dobinson (9) & Abigail Cligg (9)
Tedburn St Mary Primary School

THINGS THAT GO CRASH AND BANG IN THE NIGHT

The running night,
It almost splashes,
The night passes,
Howl,
Crash,
Bang,
What is it?
'I am coming!' I shouted,
(When I mean I am going)
Then I hear a gallop,
I crash into a tree,
Then . . .

Richard Manning (10)
Tedburn St Mary Primary School

THE WOODS AT NIGHT

As the phantom of the wood passed,
As the wind whistles through my hair,
Bang, as poachers passed,
Crack as the ice gives way,
The black dot swims in the puddle,
The phantom flies and you hear the birds' cries,
Otters splash in the dew,
Weird creep goes through the wood,
A mysterious cold chill goes through the woods,
A deadly scream echoes through the woods.

Daniel Sharland (9)
Tedburn St Mary Primary School

SEA POEM

Big whales wading,
White waves fading,
Misty sea spraying,
Tripping tide fraying.

Dolphins dip merrily,
Sharks search hungrily,
Silently spume glides,
Crazy crabs hide.

Wild wind waves,
Passing people bathe,
Flat fish sway,
Seals slip away.

Kayleigh Lucas (9)
Tedburn St Mary Primary School

WE WENT TO THE WOOD ONE NIGHT

We went to the wood one night
And saw a creaky, creepy castle.
The whistling wind howled through the branches.

We went to the wood one night
And saw the moon's reflection shining down
On the cool stream.
The trees swayed in the breeze.
We went to the wood one night.

David Rasaiah (9) & Chris Woods (9)
Tedburn St Mary Primary School

THE ECHO OF THE WOOD

The dark, dingy sky
overlooks the wood.

Forest fern floor freezes,
I plunge my foot onto the crunchy floor.

The wind whistles through my hair.

Owls swoop swiftly through the chilled air,
a howling hoot hovers above my head.

A river flows freely,
fishes jump, splash.

The wind whistles through my hair.

I can hear an echo from the distance,
it's saying 'help' from a dog's yelp.

There's a beat of horses feet,
there's a bang and a crash.

The wind whistles through my hair.

Katy Johnson (9) & Meghan McCrory (10)
Tedburn St Mary Primary School

WITCH'S CAVERN

Inside the witch's cavern,
Dark, cold and scary,
I see a witch circling round her misty cauldron
Putting in slime and dead frogs' legs.
I am screaming inside,
Although outside of me I daren't make a sound,
Or otherwise the witch would hear me
And I might end up in the misty cauldron.
The air is full of spells and chants
The witch mutters beneath her breath,
Even though these are very soft whispers,
They stab me in the heart like 1000 knives.
Her nose sticks out like a wolf howling by the lonely moon,
Her face is covered by warts and boils
And her lips are full with cracks.
The cauldron is bubbling with pale orange and bright yellow
And the witch is pouring bats' eyes inside the cauldron,
Stirring with a wooden spoon.
The witch tries hard to stir the potion.

Kim Saddler (11)
The Maynard School

HORSES AT KES TOR

Galloping over the wild, tall grass,
The three white horses go,
Forward and free across the moor,
Their tails like rivers flow.

Strong as lions in jungles,
Racehorses without a course,
Not picture-postcard ponies,
But rapid energy, in the form of a horse.

Feral horses with tangled manes,
Faster than steeple chasers,
Never again shall I see beauty
As graceful and free as these racers.

They leave with thundering hooves,
Galloping swiftly together.
I must not look away,
Or I'd lose their magic forever.

Esther Tillson (10)
The Maynard School

CHOCOLATE

I stare for a while.
I see that the wrapper is shiny.
I pick it up and hold it tight.
I open it slowly,
Enjoying every minute.
I tear the wrapper,
I smell rich, smooth, chocolate.
My mouth is watering,
I take a bite,
My face lights up with joy.
It tastes absolutely amazing!
I chew slowly
And I attempt to swallow.
I feel the chocolate slowly
Run down my throat.
I eat another piece,
Then another,
I feel myself feeling very sick.
I close the wrapper and
Save it for later!

Lucy Bayliss (11)
The Maynard School

WILDLIFE

The foxes run wild in the long grass,
The rabbits sniff and then run away,
The wild horses run against the wind,
Their manes flicker out of their faces.
The mice scurry along the floor,
Owls screech as it gets darker,
The mice scuttle away into their holes,
The moon shines down brightly
As a badger emerges out of his sett.
First its nose, then its body.
It scuttles along, sniffing all the time
Until a fox sniffs it out.
The chase is on between the badger and the fox.
The badger loses as more foxes arrive,
The foxes have gone so out comes the grass snake,
Smoothly sliding across the ground.
It disappears as fast as it arrived.
An owl comes again and screeches,
Swoops down and catches a mouse with his razor sharp claws,
Silently it flies up with no noise at all,
Off into the horizon it flies.
A bat's eyes open and stare into nowhere,
Suddenly it flutters out.
It is almost camouflaged in the darkness.
It flies into a tree and there it rests.
The clearing becomes silent as it turns back into day
And now out come the day creatures
And everything starts again.

Katy Woolley (11)
The Maynard School

SEASONS

Spring is wonderful
To the big, blue whales,
To the little brown mice,
To the medium-sized cows that swish their tails.
Spring is so soft, kind and nice.

Summer is great,
I love to swim in the sea,
To see all the fish swim so free,
To have a barbecue on the beach,
To be out of school so the teachers can't teach.

Autumn is pretty,
The leaves so bright.
All different colours, red, yellow, brown and gold,
Oh what a fantastic sight,
They all stand out ever so bold.

Winter is beautiful,
To see the snow falling,
To hear the church bells calling . . .
Christmas Eve, Christmas Eve,
Everyone dressed warmly from foot to sleeve.

Before you know it
It's a new year,
So start the poem again,
Have no fear,
Get ready for spring rain!

Jennifer Doe (10)
The Maynard School

THE WORLD OUTSIDE MY BEDROOM WINDOW!

I wake up one morning and look out of my bedroom window,
there's dew on the grass and frost on the trees.
There is mist everywhere and it is trying to cover the
wonderful and amazing sunrise,
the leaves on the trees float and glide off the branches, as it
is now windy winter!
The flowers have all closed up and the petals have dried up
and fallen to the ground,
the petals that have dried up are being carried away by the
horrible strong wind.
The animals are going into hibernation.
I can see the rabbits hop into their warm and cosy burrow
and I can see the hedgehogs crawl slowly and then stop,
and curl themselves into balls.
All the children outside are dressed up extremely warm and
they have many layers of clothes on.
Now the rain is starting to fall and all of the children are
running back to their own houses.
The rain runs down my bedroom window and it looks like
the grass has got very muddy and wet,
if I went outside on the mud I think I would slip and skid on
the disgusting mud!
The cars are driving very slowly as the roads are very slippery
and icy.
There is a child riding on his bike and he isn't even wearing
a helmet.
Now I can see the boy's dad riding along after him and now the
boy has just fallen off his bike.
His dad has helped him up and he looks all right, he isn't crying!
My next-door neighbour is walking her dog and her dog
is a Labrador.
The Labrador is very friendly and it's called Bonnie.
Oh look, my granny has arrived outside our house,
I expect my mum will let her in.

I think I will get dressed now,
I'm going to shut my curtains while I get dressed and then
after I get dressed I will go and see Granny.
I expect that Granny has brought me some chocolate or some sweets,
I think looking out of the window is great as you can see what
everyone else is doing.
Looking out of the window is like looking at a totally new,
different world than my bedroom!

Charlotte McDermid (11)
The Maynard School

WHAT IS IT?

What's cold, chilled and icy?
What numbs your throat with pain?
What slithers around your mouth?
What's it called? What is it?

What comes in succulent flavours?
Sweet strawberry and tasty toffee?
What comes with nuts and chocolate chips on top?
What's it called? What is it?

What tastes creamy, delicious and bliss?
What tastes luscious and rather sweet?
What looks appetising and really mouth-watering?
What's it called? What is it?

What's scrumptious, flavoursome and tasty?
What's full-flavoured and really sapid?
What is it? Can you guess?
Of course you can, it's ice-cream!

Roxanne Saunders (11)
The Maynard School

THE NIGHT SKY

It is full of twinkling stars,
Magical,
Amazing,
Beautiful.
The stars shine out so brightly!
When snow has fallen,
Little flowers poke through
Like diamonds in the snow!
The stars look so close,
So tiny,
Like mere fireflies
Or water drops.
They're so pretty,
Sparkling in the night.
Bright, twinkling little specks,
The sky's jewels
As they twinkle round the moon.
I look up to them.
Magic is everywhere.
I can't feel it now,
But sometimes I can!
When the wind rustles through the trees
And the crickets sing, then I can feel it!

Claudia Shaw (10)
The Maynard School

THE MOON

The moon is a place of no life
With craters as a surface.
It sits silently in space waiting in hope.
The moon is a place of no life,
With holes going down beyond its core.
Its bumps and rocks look like pearls in the sun.
The moon is a place of no life
With a haunting feeling everywhere.
It has dead volcanoes that are never to erupt again.
The moon is a place of no life,
With a dark side as cold as ice
And a hot side as hot as a desert.
The moon is a place of no life
Which orbits the Earth like a satellite
That will never come to life again!

Sarah Quicke (11)
The Maynard School

CATS

Cats, cats,
big cats, small cats,
loud cats, soft cats,
Siamese, tabbies,
black cats, ginger cats,
prancing cats, slinking cats.
Burmese, Persian,
screeching cats, mewing cats,
cuddly cats, crazy cats,
tomcats, wild cats,
white cats, grey cats,
cats, cats.

Pippa Black (10)
The Maynard School

THE SUN'S ASHES

Blazing red and maroon,
Scarlet and saffron flaming,
Brilliant explosions of flickering fire.

Anger and fear hidden in the deep orange,
Fiery lights with dancing flares
Leaping lava with excitable rage.

Boiling gases, ready to explode,
Black holes deep and dangerous,
The flames ready to shrivel up anything.

A sphere of heat and a burning ball of anger and fury.
A sparkling stellar of hot, glistening, glowing light,
A volcano ready to erupt
With nothing to do but rage,
the sun is stationary,
With bits of orbitation.

Dusk falls and the sun sets,
leaving a trail of bright ashes behind.
When the ashes reach the ground,
All the lights go off and everything is motionless.
Everything has gone.

Naomi Pankhurst (11)
The Maynard School

PLAYGROUND WAR

War is the name of what we declare.
Boys against girls, now I think that's fair.
Now we're all getting ready for our playground war,
The boys think they're stronger, but the girls have got more.

Football! Football! Is the boys game,
It drives most of us girls insane.
Skipping! Skipping! Is what we want to play,
But the boys nearly always say 'No way!'

'Charge!' shout the girls and 'Charge!' shout the boys,
We all start to run and make lots of noise.
Crash, bang, wallop and wallop, crash, bang.
'You can't beat us!' 'Yes we can!'

Rosa Bonifacii (11)
Tipton St John Primary School

MY PUPPY

'Woof' the dog yaps out
As his slimy nose rubs you,
Licking on your hand.

Jumping up excitedly,
Chewing up my sock,
'Spot!'

Laura Clapp (11)
Tipton St John Primary School

RIVER

Splash, splosh, shouts the river,
It's so cold it will make you quiver.
Water splashing on the banks aside,
Birds swooping through the sky.

Polluted water crackling through the city,
People that stomp by don't think it's pretty.
Stones that fall in make a plopping sound,
But other stones smack the ground.

Dogs jumping in make the water go ka-splash,
The owners throw a ball in which makes a great clash.
Sometimes they have waterfalls which make the water foam,
You find some sizzling rubbish in it, once I found a comb.

Asher Smyth (9)
Tipton St John Primary School

THE RIVER

Splish-splash, splash-splish, gushing down the river.
Splosh-swish, swish-splash, flowing down the river.
Drip-drop, drop-drip, where it goes no one knows.
Trickle-tickle, tickle-trickle squeezing between my toes.

Run along to the river bank up to the crashing weir,
Look it carries on along up here.
Don't stop, run gently along here.
Look, look, there's a bridge, but the water carries on
                                        up here.

Emma Carruthers (10)
Tipton St John Primary School

LATE

'You're late' said Miss,
'The bell has gone.
Dinner numbers done
And work's begun,
So what have you got to say for yourself?'

'It's like this, I'm sorry Miss,
My brother was sick over this
And my sister fell over a bell,
My mum tripped into a water well.
My dad was stuck in a great big truck,
I was going along at the speed of light
When a dog jumped out and gave me a bite.
I was rushed to hospital (on a stretcher)
And I bumped into a boxer called Retcher.
He gave me a look and walked away.
I was a daydreamer Miss, today
Anyway I was in the school (at last)
And it's only quarter past.'

'Ok, you win
And put your homework in the bin.
Sit down and write your story,
And go over there and sit by that boy.'

'Um, Miss, I don't have anything to write about!'

Susannah Moore (11)
Tipton St John Primary School

LATE

'You're late,' said Miss,
'The bell has gone, dinner numbers done
And work's begun.
What have you got to say for yourself?

'Well, it's like this Miss,
I grabbed my bag and my coat,
left the house and ran into a goat.
It bit my arm, then my bum,
Then suddenly from behind the clouds appeared the sun.
The goat ran away in a flash,
I looked at my watch - must dash.
I was half way here,
Getting close to the weir
Until I met a sweet little toad.
It looked at me with green eyes,
So I gave it one of my pies.
Then I was sucked into a spaceship
And there stood aliens with big blue lips,
Some striped and some covered in dots,
I tell you Miss, there were lots and lots.
They dropped me off in the playground
Then I ran in here, hopefully without a sound,
And here I am now.'

'Yes, yes, sit down and next time say you're sorry
For disturbing all the class and get on with your story fast!'

'But Miss, I have nothing to write about!'

Megan Thomas (11)
Tipton St John Primary School

PLANT CYCLE

Plants are around us everywhere,
Just take the time to stop and stare.
Flowers, bushes, trees and weeds,
All of these began as seeds.
First the seed puts out some roots,
Followed closely by the shoots.
Now germination has begun,
The shoots grow upward to the sun.
Next the cooling April showers,
Help to form the pretty flowers.
Flowers bloom and then they set,
Their life is still not over yet.
Seed will drop, fall to the ground,
And so the cycle goes on round.

Claire Rule (10)
Tipton St John Primary School

WHAT CAN YOU FIND IN YOUR GARDEN?

What can you find in your garden?
Do you know it could be a zoo?
A hedgehog, a vixen, a blue tit,
A badger, an owl, a kitten or two.
There are also lots of insects,
Crawling along the ground.
Woodlice, beetles, worms or ants,
Every creature here can be found.

Neal Clapp (10)
Two Moors Primary School

QUIZ SHOWS

Wheel of Fortune,
Spin the wheel.

Supermarket Sweep,
Get money from the till.

Catch Phrase,
Find the phrase.

Family Fortunes,
Entertain.

Fifteen to One,
Use your brain.

Who Wants To Be A Millionaire,
Fifty-fifty.

Count Down,
Numeracy plus literacy.

Meg Menheneott (11)
Two Moors Primary School

FAMILY

F   is for father
A   is for attention
M   is for mother
I   is for independent
L   is for love
Y   is for young

Rhiannon Babb (11)
Two Moors Primary School

I SAW

I saw a dog
eating a hog.
I saw a pig,
fat as a twig.
I saw a man
shaped as a frying pan.
I saw a lamb
as fat as a van.
I saw a sheep,
that couldn't bleat.
I saw a frog,
long as a log.
I saw a cow,
go miaow.
I saw a bug
having a hug.
I saw ants
wearing pants.
I saw a toad
that was bold.
I saw a bee
tall as a tree.
I saw ET
use BT.
I saw a rat
shaped as a cricket bat.
Lastly I saw a goat
driving a boat.

Daniel Cottrell (10)
Two Moors Primary School

RAIN

Trickle, trickle,
Drip, drip,
The rain is coming down.
It's like a tear drop,
It's so depressing,
It's happening all over town.
I'm inside in the warm looking out on the rain,
It's cold and wet,
Yesterday it was warm.
Why does it rain?
Why does the weather change?
I cannot explain the rain.

Cally Harris (10)
Two Moors Primary School

THE MONSTER

One night I called Monster Ted
because under my bed
was a monster
with big, blurry eyes
as big as pork pies.
He had two grins
stuck on his face with pins,
with no nose,
instead a water hose.
I turned on the light,
it was a teddy!

Sam Isaacs (11)
Two Moors Primary School

WHAT IF?

What if my bum was red?
What if my mum was dead?
What if I got stuck down the bog?
What if I ate a dog?
What if I got hurt in a fight?
What if my cat ate a light?
What if my mum ate a bull?
What if I missed a day off school?
What if my hair was blue?
What if there was a green bubaloo?
What if the sky was pink?
What if I couldn't think?
What if the sunlight went?
What if I wandered into Kent?
What if I touched a cloud that was fluffy?
What if I got scared while I was watching Buffy?
What if I looked up at the sky?
What if people were trying to spy?
What if my bum was red?

Nikita Harrison (10)
Two Moors Primary School

POODLES

Perfectly permed with bows in their hair,
walk around with a glorious air.
Very pink with pearly teeth,
probably goes to the poodle parlour every week.
Very spoilt and fluffy, probably sleeps on a velvet pouffe,
always eats meat on a seat,
but never out in the rain.

Deborah Toon (10)
Two Moors Primary School

I WONDER WHERE THE SKY ENDS?

I wonder where the sky ends?
Does it end after Pluto with a wobbly line,
Or maybe with a straight gold line?
It could be a piece of metal to make it round,
I wonder, wonder, where the sky ends?

I wonder where the sky ends?
It might go on for ever and ever,
Or it could just be a large box?
Maybe it's from the sun to Pluto,
Outlined in red?
I wonder, wonder, where the sky ends?

I wonder where the sky ends?
Do you know, oh please tell me.
I often look up.
Oh I wonder, wonder, where the sky ends?

Natalie Burnage (10)
Two Moors Primary School

WHEN I WAS WALKING

When I was walking,
I saw a dog racing a hog.
When I was walking,
I saw a bee dancing with a flea.
When I was walking,
I saw a tiger drinking Budweiser.
When I was walking,
I saw a frog using the bog.

Robert Willis (10)
Two Moors Primary School

Away With The Alphabet

A is for aeroplane high up in the sky
B is for Billy eating his pie
C is for Claire singing in a band
D is for Derek playing in the sand
E is for Eric writing a story
F is for Fulham hunting for glory
G is for Graham who is ten feet tall
H is for Harry who ran into a wall
K is for Kim who lived in a bin
L is for Len who got kicked in the shin
M is for Munich who lost the cup
N is for Nottingham who aren't going up.

Chris Baker (11)
Two Moors Primary School

Stars

Gleaming, glistening, glittery stars
Shining on me,
Listening to the twinkles up above,
Shining on me,
Up in the sky so high,
Shining on me,
They're twinkling in the sky,
Shining on me,
They stay out until tomorrow,
Shining on me,
Why are you looking at those shiny stars?
Shining on me.

Daisy Clark (11)
Two Moors Primary School

THE SKODA

Clonkety-clank, clappidy-bang!
That's the sound of old Bob's Skoda
That's always conking out on the M5.
Clonkety-clank, clappidy-bang!
There goes the engine and exhaust.
Clonkety-clank, clappidy-bang!
Poor old Bob.
He's never had a decent car,
But maybe next time he won't buy a Skoda.
Clonkety-clank, clappidy-bang!

Nico Cruwys (10)
Two Moors Primary School

I WONDER

I wonder if the sky will fall down?
I wonder if I will drown?
I wonder if I am going to go to town?
I wonder if my mum will get me that gown?
I wonder!

Emily Warren (11)
Two Moors Primary School

MY BROTHER

My brother is a pest even though he thinks he's the best.
My brother is annoying even though he is boring.
My brother is a pain when he stands there in the rain.
My brother's so insane, he's got no brain!

Linsey Williams (10)
Two Moors Primary School

THE SUNSET

The sunset has many beautiful colours such as
orange, yellow, red, blue, purple and pink.
It's like a colourful, velvety, soft, squidgy pillow
stretched out across the horizon.
It makes me think of crisp, sunny days with
green grass, lots of flowers and children
playing in outdoor pools.
It reminds me of people sunbathing and people
                              enjoying themselves.
It reminds me of holidays and birds chirping
                              in the trees.

Bonnie Williams (11)
Two Moors Primary School

DREAMS I'LL NEVER FORGET

I saw the sun,
then I began to run.

As I was running,
I heard the soft sound
of sand and pebbles.

My hands were sore
and my feet were wet.
These are the things
I will never forget.

Kerry Harvey (11)
Two Moors Primary School

POPPIES

Where people die,
Poppies grow,
Field on field,
Row on row.

Poppies, poppies,
Remembrance Day,
Symbolise blood,
Where the dead lay.

Two minutes silence
On the eleventh,
Our thoughts are for
Those who died.

Rebecca Lee (10)
Two Moors Primary School

THE RAINFOREST

The trees in the rainforest whisper secrets,
The predators stalk as prey shuffle their feet nervously,
Snakes slither silently along the ground
And spiders hustle and rustle in their daily bustle to find food.
As night closes in it leaves a red, rosy glow on the ground.
But only half of the rainforest sleeps
As the other half wakes up.
Over again the cycle goes,
Predator stalks prey.
The rainforest never sleeps.

Dawn Toner (11)
Two Moors Primary School

THE MOON GEM

Reflections of a winter's moon,
Sparkling in the silver light,
Glittering in the night.

Brighter than the brightest star,
How I wonder what you are.

Stephen Hill (11)
Winkleigh Primary School

CATNAP

Miaow, miaow, I'm warm and cosy,
Snuggled up in my owner's bed,
With the lovely food that
I have been fed,
So now I'm really not in the mood
To wander about and be nosy.

Miranda Gent (9)
Winkleigh Primary School

MY DOG POPPY 2

P   oppy ran away on the strike of midnight
O   n the strike of the millennium
P   oppy was lovely, black and white she was
P   oppy got a bit annoying sometimes
Y   et I still miss her terribly

Gemma Anstey (10)
Winkleigh Primary School

WAR AND PEACE

Bang! Bang
Go the guns!
Bang
Go the tanks, ready to fire.
Shwo, shwo
Starts the rotor of the helicopter,
And worst of all, the blood.

Zzzzzzz
The sound of a chain saw cutting down a tree.
Raaaaaa
The sound of a tiger's last roar.

Stop this and have a good time on Earth.

Alex Todd (8)
Winkleigh Primary School

UNDER THE SEA

Oh no! It's my bed time,
But . . . I don't go to sleep.
I put on my diving suit,
My snorkel, breather tank and glasses.
I dive down deep under the sea
To find my mermaid castle.
My castle is a beautiful place,
I stay there all the time.
It's so much fun all the year round
Until . . . 'Lights out.'
Oh, trust my mum to spoil it!

Virginia Reeve-Hodgson (10)
Winkleigh Primary School

SPRING SEASON

S ummer's on its way
P eople are sunbathing
R oundabout now new lambs are being born
I like going on holiday
N ew beginnings, starting again
G oing to have a lovely time

Sophie Popham (10)
Winkleigh Primary School

ROBIN

Sometimes in my garden
I can see a little robin.
He flutters around all day and night,
He mainly flutters in the light.
Sometimes in my garden,
I can see a little robin and a bee.

Benjamin Riches (10)
Winkleigh Primary School

THE SEA

The sea is beautiful, the sea is bright,
It glistens and gleams, all day and night.
Bass and gobies, sand eels and squid,
You can buy them all, for only five quid.

Liam Marshall (8)
Winkleigh Primary School

RIVER

Lushing, rushing, gushing, river.
Whirling, swirling, hurling, river,
Grasping on to nature.
Below, trout jumping for life,
Above, bears catch trout
In the foaming wild river.
Below, crayfish are fighting,
Above, a fisherman prepares bait.
Uh oh! Here comes a pike!
Too late! Fishes meet their doom
In this wild, desolate river.

Edward Knight (8)
Winkleigh Primary School

STARS

Shining so bright,
Twinkling all night,
All are asleep,
Waiting peacefully
For alarms to bleep.

Thomas Shacklock (8)
Winkleigh Primary School

THE SUMMER

In the summer
The sunlight glows,
Hits the mirror like glistening gold,
Then it shines into people's eyes,
Shining away till the sunlight dies.

Sally Rogers (10)
Winkleigh Primary School

MILLENNIUM MEMORIES

We have been through two thousand years
People laughing, shouting hooray
You should be happy, so we don't want tears
So forget your past and look at today.

> The sparkling lights are in the sky
> People have the giggles and too much to eat
> The snow comes racing with the sleet
> For everyone this is a fantastic treat.

Fireworks come sprinkling out of the sky
I watched, amazed, with a smile on my face
As the fireworks fly,
They repeat and give chase.

> At dawn the sun rises slowly
> A New Year has come
> The world has turned a new roly poly
> The old year has gone numb.

Susanna Ward (10)
Winkleigh Primary School

TRAINS

The train's whizzing by,
Faster and faster it goes.
Nearer and nearer to the station,
Now it's in sight, squeeeak . . .
It's slowing down.
Squeeeak . . . it's stopped.

Robert North (9)
Winkleigh Primary School

A Sparkling Night

See the stars sparkle bright,
And the moon, brilliant white,
Dream of what will happen tomorrow,
The good, the bad, happiness and sorrow,
A slit in the curtains, light shines in,
And from the dining room a humorous din,
The wind it howls and howls outdoors,
The rain it rattles and pours and pours,
But the stars still sparkle bright,
Isn't it a wonderful night!
In the living room a fire is alight,
Warm as toast on this cold night.

Emily Heggadon (8)
Winkleigh Primary School

Teeth

Brushing your teeth day and night,
Keeps the dentist out of sight.
If you eat an apple a day
It will keep the doctor away!

Mathieu Lomax (7)
Winkleigh Primary School

Football 2000

Footballs speeding to the back of the nets
As the football players look like little sets
Couldn't the players score a goal,
Instead of just standing by the pole?

Alex Mark Brett (9)
Winkleigh Primary School

TRI

My dog Tri has three brown patches
His body is white with speckles and splodges.
Long ears fly, as he leaps and bounds.
He's going to be a hunting dog
To help keep down numbers
Of rabbits, to help stop myxomatosis.
Being a puppy he chews things up.
The only way to keep him quiet
Is to fuss him,
Or to shut him away with his food
Which is soon gone.

Lucy Marshall (10)
Winkleigh Primary School

THE BUTTERFLY DANCE

Flitter, flutter,
Around the flowers we go,
Never a mutter,
While the colours flow,
Up, down and along,
Flitter, flutter,
After winter's gone,
Flitter, flutter,
Painting the sky,
And from Earth,
'Oh my!' does fly.

Hannah Norman (9)
Winkleigh Primary School

BIRDS OF MY GARDEN

It's springtime in my garden,
Lots of birds come in,
Like the blackbirds, blue tits, and the odd chaffinch.

It's summertime in my garden,
Lots of birds come in,
Like swifts, house martins and thrushes.

It's autumn time in my garden,
Lots of birds come in,
Like starlings, wagtails and sparrows.

It's wintertime in my garden
Lots of birds come in
Like crows, robins and jackdaws
And sometimes a pair of doves.

Amy Tyler (9)
Winkleigh Primary School

TRAIN

The train is going like lightning,
Running along the rails,
Along the countryside,
Into the tunnel
Nearing a station, stopping at last.

Luke Gordon Winsor (11)
Winkleigh Primary School

RABBITS

Rabbits, rabbits, soft as snow,
Rabbits, rabbits, here we go.

Rabbits, rabbits, here and there,
Rabbits, rabbits, everywhere.

Rabbits, rabbits, all around,
Rabbits, rabbits, underground.

Rabbits, rabbits, come and play,
On this beautiful summer's day.

Tracey Hutchings (10)
Winkleigh Primary School

SCHOOL'S OUT

School's out, fun time in!
Tomorrow we play netball and
We're going to win.
My friend is coming round to play
But my big brother says, 'Go away!'
Dinner time is great
Dinner time is fun
Especially when we're playing in the sun.

Larisa Fay (9)
Winkleigh Primary School

SOOTY, MY BLACK RABBIT

Sooty, my black rabbit,
Has small droopy ears,
His eyes are like little spots
And he's really soft.

His nose smells the food,
When I come to feed him,
He always likes the carrots
And the dry food too.

But he never smiles
Not to anyone.

Katrina Brook (9)
Winkleigh Primary School

THE OWL

The owl wakes up when the sun has gone,
Night has awoken, the owl is about,
He takes off into the night looking for food,
When he sees a mouse he dives to the ground,
The mouse hides and the owl flies,
Now hungry and thirsty he finds a lake,
The owl has a mouse then he flies home,
Eats then rests then flies into the night sky
And is never seen again.

Amanda Briant (9)
Winkleigh Primary School

OWL

Hooting through the night
Scuffle of animals
Disturbing sounds
Down on the ground
Whooshing, swooping,
See the shadows
Still,
Not moving
Or shaking.

Catch it
Rip it apart
Swallow it down
Eat the meat
Cough up the bones
Never make a sound.

Drifting to your hollow
Cuddling up
Plumage soft
Going to your dreams.

Jessica Watkins (9)
Woodbury CE Primary School

THE OWL

Cruel, soundless, the owl,
he flies silently.
Quiet, mysterious, the owl,
he spots a vole.
Haunting, ghostly, the owl,
he swoops.
Noiseless, frightening, the owl,
he clamps.
Swift, gliding, the owl,
he rips.
Spectral, killing, the owl,
he digests.
Keeper of the forests,
the owl,
he stares.
Shrieking eerily,
the owl,
he hoots.
Wise, majestic, the owl,
he's king.

Daryl Price (9)
Woodbury CE Primary School

THE HUNTER

Awakes the grave,
Awakes the sky,
Awakes the doom,

Alive the mice,
Alive the voles,
Alive the moles,

Awakes the cold,
Awakes the killer,
Awakes the owl,

Cry the mice,
Scream the voles,
Gasp the moles,

Stalks the owl,
Swoops the hunter,
Plunge the claws,

Hushed the mice,
Silent the voles,
Murdered the moles.

Jasmine Bowden (8)
Woodbury CE Primary School

THE OWL

The owl swoops down to snatch its prey.
It's scared to show its face in the day.
It stretches its pinions from tree to tree.
All small creatures need to flee.
It flaps its wings over its meal.
It screeches savagely for the kill.
It longs to go back so it can sleep.
Hide from harsh daylight, dreaming deep.

Michael Kalisch (8)
Woodbury CE Primary School

SWEET LOVE

As I sat on the bench,
The love of my life walked past,
My eyes turned to hearts.
My hands turned to stone,
Then I started to sweat.
As he walked away
Butterflies were flying in my tummy,
My legs went floppy.
And I almost fell over.
So the next bench I saw I sat down.
I took a deep breath.
My heart started to pound
Then I tried to walk home.

Bethany Hall (11)
Yeo Valley Primary School

LOVE

The girl stood like a ray of sunshine,
her head spinning,
her heart bouncing with the butterflies in her stomach.
She felt like a sun of gold, floating in the air,
she had never felt like this before.
Her eyes gazed into his as they cuddled.
They sat on the beach holding hands,
as they watched the sun go down.
Her heart stopped,
as she gazed at him,
her head spinning once more,
her heart bouncing with the butterflies in her stomach.

Kim Rogers (10)
Yeo Valley Primary School

A STORM

A storm is a raging bull,
ready to strike its prey.
His feet racing to the rocks,
like trains on tracks.
His eyes lit up the colour of red.
His speed knocked down his prey.
His wounded feast,
howled with anger.
Drool dripped down with hunger.

Bethany Angell (10)
Yeo Valley Primary School

ICE

One night I woke
I looked out of the window,
Where the pond should be,
I saw a round piece of glass,
Glistening in the moonlight.
When I looked closer the glass had
Formed in a sheet of foil,
Which looked very much like a skating ring.

Katie L Pink (10)
Yeo Valley Primary School

ICE

One icy night a woman had a fright.
In the middle of the night,
She took some ice,
Thought it was nice.
Ice is cold, ice is hard,
Shiny and slippery, ice is cracked,
Ice is nice, ice is on roofs, ice is everywhere . . .

Latisha Collins (9)
Yeo Valley Primary School

THE ICE CAME LAST NIGHT

The ice came last night
Creeping silently through
Didn't make a single noise
Ice is sharp daggers falling, breaking
Ghost slips on the ice.

Josh Yeo (9)
Yeo Valley Primary School

LONELY

I was all alone,
Standing in the playground, like I was invisible.
I was jealous,
Watching everybody playing with their friends.

I was in the corridor,
Everybody pushing me out of the way,
I started to cry,
No one noticed me there, I felt like I was never born.

I went to see my best friend,
She just left me out of all the games.
I saw my cousin,
He just pushed me away and didn't notice me at all.

I went home crying,
My mum didn't notice I was around.
I just stormed upstairs,
I just went to bed crying, hoping it would all go away.

Claire Harris (11)
Yeo Valley Primary School

MY LOVE

I was sitting there as if someone had hit me with cupid's arrows.
My eyes were wide open with gold hearts,
I felt like I was the queen of the sun.

Pink and golden hearts were floating around mine and his heads.
I was in a world of my own, floating with him.
My heart took a leap as he looked up at me.

Terri Sheppard (11)
Yeo Valley Primary School

LOVE!

The girl stood and stared into his eyes.
She felt like she had little hearts hovering round her head.
She had never felt like this before.
It felt like she was going to fly away with the butterflies.
Her heart started to pound
As he walked past her.

Laura Matthewson (10)
Yeo Valley Primary School

MY FEAR

My fear is as quick as a flash,
It puts my life in a pot,
It puts me in a cage,
It traps me in a room,
It lives in my body.

Jennifer White (9)
Yeo Valley Primary School

UPSET

Her eyes were filled with blue water
As her face was pale as I looked
Her sunken mouth and shallow eyes
As her face went blue.

Kylie Bamsby (11)
Yeo Valley Primary School

I Think My Friend Is Angry!

My friend's head blew up like a volcano at its worst,
Raindrops jumped from his head like lava,
Beams of red shot out from his eyes,
His eyes were as red as blood.

He then ran around the playground like a wild bull,
With steam of death coming from his ears and nose.

He aimed at anyone red,
And hit them when he caught up,
His hair was now fire,
Then a dinner lady wearing red, walked across the playground,
He turned around and . . .

Miss, watch out!

Drew Owens (11)
Yeo Valley Primary School

The Plodder

The fog is an elephant,
plodding through the jungle,
spreading out its grey mist
like the skin of its own kind
stretched throughout the jungle floor,
laying out its wet morning dew
on all of the lower plants of the jungle,
taking up all of the space it can get at.

The plants' leaves sway
under the soft touch of the fog elephant's trunk.

Matthew Hitchins (11)
Yeo Valley Primary School

THE SUNSHINE

The sunshine is a princess,
A weather of beauty,
And royalness.

It brightens up, such a beauty,
It glistens no matter what,
It has many admirers,
Just like a princess.

As royal as it is,
It still shines with happiness,
And laughter.

It is a gift of cheer and high hopes,
For the future,
And present.

Samantha Lewis (11)
Yeo Valley Primary School

IN THE PLAYGROUND

I went out to play tomorrow.
I was sitting on the bench running.
I was playing football while bouncing a ball.
I was at the top of the playground at the bottom.
I was writing while playing tig.
I was running while walking.
I was laughing while crying!

Mark Palmer (11)
Yeo Valley Primary School

MY DAY

I was doing my science
When I was at home
I looked at my mum
When it was my dad
I started crying
When I was laughing
When I woke up in the evening
I brushed my teeth
With my toes
I washed my face
With my socks
At school we did numeracy
When it was literacy
And I wrote with my hair
And when I got home
I went swimming
In the circus!

Laura Ellis (10)
Yeo Valley Primary School

THE SUN

The crimson orb with an illuminated glow.
A two pence floats in the air with a fiery heat.
The shining flare in the sky.
A golden globe way up high.

Nathan Windsor (10)
Yeo Valley Primary School

THE SUN

The round hot ball wakes up to warm the world.
It is so dazzling it burns the sea.
A speck of flame can bring the hot ball to life,
But when it's time to go it goes down in a colourful sea.
When night comes you can see it glitter in the moonlight.

Emma Mason (10)
Yeo Valley Primary School

THE SUN

It is like a blazing sphere in a puddle of soapy warm water.
It is a light bulb suspended in the summer's sky.
The bouncing ball says from up, up high
'How high shall I rise today?'
The penny was hot today but it faded away.

Esther Elizabeth Prosser (10)
Yeo Valley Primary School

TORNADO

The giant hoover is sucking up its food.
There is a roaring giant saying 'I want my food!'
The giant puffed a demolishing puff.
The giant is sneezing and blows everything away.
It is a tasty twizzler.

Sam Harley (10)
Yeo Valley Primary School

FEAR AND ANGER

My fear
My fear is like dark blood, my fear smells like raw fish.
My fear is shot out of a gun with whimpering surrounding me.
My fear takes away my fun, away from all my life.

My anger
My anger takes away my friends, my anger leaves me hopeless.
My anger smells like rotten chips.
My anger is really something you don't want to mess with.

Rachel Wait (10)
Yeo Valley Primary School

ANGER

Angry in the night, night sky
red as a fire
like sour red berries
litter taking over
like a thorny branch
it can get big, big, big, big
and then explode.

Sophie Hawkins (10)
Yeo Valley Primary School